The Life Givers

Books by David Hendin

The Life Givers
Guide to Ancient Jewish Coins
Death as a Fact of Life
The Doctors' Save-Your-Heart Diet (with Aileen Claire)
Save Your Child's Life!
Everything You Need to Know About Abortion

THE LIFE GIVERS

by David Hendin

WILLIAM MORROW AND COMPANY, INC.
NEW YORK   1976

920.961
H 495 l

Printed in the United States of America.

1 2 3 4 5 80 79 78 77 76

Library of Congress Cataloging in Publication Data

Hendin, David.
  The life givers.
  Includes index.
  1. Physicians—United States—Biography. I. Title.
R153.H46   610'.92'4 [B]   75-42119
ISBN 0-688-03035-1

Book design: H. Roberts

For Sandra

Contents

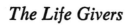

The Life Givers

1 Who Are the Life Givers?

Here are the stories of six physicians whose ideas and discoveries have, in a very real sense, extended or enhanced the courses of the lives of millions of human beings. The life of each reader of this book has certainly been affected by one or more of the doctors I have taken the liberty of nicknaming the Life Givers, although I am well aware that this is not a perfect description. As one of them told me, "We doctors are only human. We do our best. But no miracles."

Please note, however, that one of Webster's definitions of "miracle" is "an unusual event, thing, or accomplishment." And in that sense, at least, there is little doubt that the reader is about to learn of six men who have accomplished miracles. Here are the stories of:

Jonas Salk, who killed the polio virus; Howard Rusk, who offered new hope for the severely handicapped; C. Walton Lillehei, who made open heart surgery possible; Irving Cooper, who froze the brain; Nathan Kline, who pioneered in drugs to combat mental illness, and John Rock, the Catholic who was one of the fathers of the birth control pill.

These six, of course, aren't the only doctors whose work has been significant, exciting, unusual. The Life Givers are only a sampling. They are not to be thought of as *the six greatest,* although they may well be *six of the greatest.* Each of their careers has been controversial in its own right, but there is little doubt that each is a true leader in his field.

It goes without saying that there are other leaders. In medicine an idea rarely exists alone, surrounded by nothingness. Instead each new idea is an addition to the current body of knowledge. Each development is an extension of the work that preceded it—and, rather than an end in itself, also part of the foundation of the work that will no doubt follow. Thus there is often a scientific and sociological climate that plays a major role in discovery. This is illustrated in the saying, no doubt true, that "America would have been discovered even without Columbus."

It is far too easy to fall into the trap of treating one person's work as alone in its uniqueness. On the other hand it's easy to imagine the dangers in attempting to acknowledge every predecessor and every colleague whose work a researcher has taken into consideration. This problem becomes even more difficult when one considers what sociologist Robert Merton has called "cryptomensia."

Cryptomensia is unconscious plagiarism, selective forgetting. The phenomenon is innocent enough, and there are many examples of it in almost every field. Two eminent poets, for example, published the same poem several years apart. One of them had read the other's work previously and then stored it in his subconscious mind. Later it was "thought up" as original. It is also said that Charles Darwin made a special point of recording unfavorable data because he had a tendency to more easily forget them.

It is quite possible that some or all of the Life Givers have been guilty of cryptomensia during their reminiscences in interviews with the author. Additional research has eliminated it whenever possible. At any rate, each of the six subjects of this book has frequently and freely acknowledged his debts to the work of others. Any curtailment or abbreviation of those connections was done by the author for the sake of continuity.

When friends and associates heard that I was researching a book on "six great contemporary physicians," they usually replied: "You mean like Christiaan Barnard?"

Barnard, no doubt, is assured a place in the history books. He might have been included here, since the choices are subjective enough. But the plan called for only one physician from the cardiovascular field; should it have been Barnard? Although his human heart transplant was the first, it was largely based on techniques devised at Stanford University by Dr. Norman Shumway, who has actually been the most successful of the heart transplanters. But Shumway's work would never have been carried out if it had not been for the "heart-lung machine." That devilishly simple device was perfected at the University of Minnesota under the direction of C. Walton Lillehei, who also pioneered many techniques of open heart surgery. Studying under Lillehei, incidentally, while much of his significant work was being done, were both Christiaan Barnard and Norman Shumway.

Each of the Life Givers performed the significant portion of his work since 1950, all of them were part of the postwar boom in important medical discovery. Each of them has worked in a different field, and they have been chosen, in part, because through their stories one can also convey much knowledge about both medical research and the particular fields of interest.

As a journalist specializing in writing about health care, I deal daily with doctors who have made discoveries or who have something significant to say. In her doctoral dissertation entitled "The Visible Scientists," Rae Goodell observed that there is a certain group of scientists which above all others remains before the public eye. Goodell has broken these into two basic groups, the "issue" scientists and the "discovery" scientists. With the possible exception of Howard Rusk, whose issue is the plight of the handicapped, the Life Givers are all "discovery" scientists, although some of them have adopted issues as well—such as Irving Cooper's deep concern with the humanity of medicine and John Rock's crusade to convert the Catholic Church to birth control advocacy.

Goodell observes that ". . . an 'issue' scientist somehow seems to have less stature than a discoverer. By definition he cannot stand on a pedestal to be admired as 'great' . . ." Yet, she adds, ". . . in a period when visibility of scientists as a whole is declining, the 'issue' scientists are the hardiest strain. . . ."

Therefore, I imagine it should not have come as such a surprise that large numbers of people have never heard—or don't recollect—the names Lillehei, Rusk, Rock, Kline, or Cooper. Everybody, of course, is familiar with Salk, who, incidentally, is the only one of the Life Givers listed by Goodell as a "visible scientist."

And even though most remember Jonas Salk, too many hear the name and recall tales of the bright young man sweating over virulent viruses in the laboratory and then, one day, shouting, "Eureka, I have found it." It was nothing like that, and, you will see, Salk himself is the first one to put dampers on such vivid imaginations.

In each of the Life Givers there is a certain roguish quality; they have unorthodox ideas, they are mavericks. And each of the six evokes a certain degree of jealousy among his colleagues, and each of them has been rejected by portions of the medical establishment at various times in his career.

This is not meant, necessarily, to sound like a condemnation of the medical establishment, whose job, after all, is to protect the public against unproven claims. "All too often, though," science writer Albert Rosenfeld observes, "resistance to innovative ideas and techniques is due not so much to protection of the public as to protection of ideas and practices in which established scientists have a large emotional investment."

Rosenfeld adds that "sometimes it is hard to get a fellow scientist even to consider a new idea with real interest—especially if it challenges some favorite idea of his own or threatens his status."

In fact, Nathan Kline, one of the Life Givers, back in 1962, coined a word to describe this phenomenon—"factifuging," or flight from the facts. In *Lancet,* a British medical journal, Kline published an article describing a number of gambits for avoiding coming to grips with new facts—particularly facts that appeared to be uncomfortably correct—while pretending to do the opposite.

Even today, years after the discoveries of most of the Life Givers, one doesn't have to look too hard to find physicians still willing to call certain colleagues "fakes," "quacks," or "publicity mongers." But the innovations made by each of the Life Givers stand in tribute to their viability as successful medical scientists.

The charges of "publicity monger" deserve added attention, for although each of the Life Givers has been thus described, the author's experience with each of them does not bear out such accusations. These men, after all, have significantly participated in the building of "better mousetraps"; thus the world, particularly the world of the media, has beaten a path to their doors. Too often they have been used by the media, instead of vice versa.

In 1971 Boyd Lewis, then head of Newspaper Enterprise Association, a news-feature service where I am employed, told me to phone Irving Cooper to find out about some fantastic new discoveries he had made about the human brain. Cooper and Lewis were close friends and neighbors. Nevertheless, Cooper put me off time and again. Finally, almost a year later, he agreed to see me. In meeting after meeting

I dragged information out of this world-renowned neurosurgeon. The information I finally gathered was so complete I felt as if I had taken a short course in neurosurgery—certainly some of the staff at St. Barnabas Hospital thought I was a doctor in training. For a period of several months I watched the surgeon operate, scrubbed my hands with him, ate with him, visited patients with him.

We finally agreed that I would write my story to coincide with a paper he was to deliver on the new work at the end of the year. I mustn't break that agreement, Cooper stressed, for release of stories before papers are presented is a practice frowned upon within the scientific community.

Because of all the time I had spent working on the Cooper story, I had confidence my reporting on the complicated details would be factual.

Little did I know that Cooper, too, recognized my new-found knowledge, for when one of the science writers for a national news magazine read my story and phoned Cooper for verification, he refused to talk to the reporter. The reporter, in fact, was referred to *me* and the story I had written for any further information that was necessary. This is not the type of behavior one expects to encounter when dealing with a "publicity hound."

"You spent months working on that story," Cooper told me later. "I wasn't about to let somebody get all of the facts and information screwed up, and make me look foolish, just because they had only an hour or so to work on the story. I knew they would basically rewrite *your* story, so I referred them to you." In the following months, of course, Cooper cooperated on request with a number of other reporters who were able to spend the time to understand and appreciate the new work he was doing. Naturally enough, Cooper, as well as the other Life Givers, likes to receive credit for work well done.

"All scientists I know sufficiently well to judge (and I

include myself in this group)," remarked stress expert Hans Selye, "are extremely anxious to have their work recognized and approved by others. . . . What is there to be ashamed of?"

When this credit is not forthcoming it can be a great frustration. Dr. Donald Effler of the Cleveland Clinic has observed that for a surgeon to be great he "must have a fierce determination to be the leader in his field. He must have a driving ego, a hunger beyond money. He must have a passion for perfectionism. He is like the actor who wants his name in lights."

It is not only the surgeons who bask in the glory of original observation and innovation. These, after all, are the focal points and goals of all scientific research. Scientists are none too happy when conflicts over priorities arise. Galileo complained about somebody who "attempted to rob me of that glory which was mine," and many other stories of scientific theft appear in the literature.

When a scientist fails to receive recognition for an original idea it can destroy him. Ignaz Semmelweis, whose general observations on the nature of infectious disease preceded both Lister and Pasteur, was spurned by his colleagues as a crank. It drove him crazy.

William Halsted, father of modern surgery in the United States, practiced at Johns Hopkins University in the late nineteenth and early twentieth centuries. He once wrote a letter to a friend complaining that "I showed Wölfler how to use cocaine [as a surgical anesthetic]. He had declared it was useless in surgery, but before I left Vienna, he published an enthusiastic article in one of the daily papers on the subject. It did not, however, occur to him to mention my name."

From these examples it is clear that the Life Givers are not the first physicians who have been jealously proud of their work, nor are they likely to be the last.

I vividly recall my first—and subsequent—readings of *The*

Microbe Hunters. De Kruif helped readers visualize Pasteur, Ehrlich, and the others rushing about their laboratories making discoveries. But he wrote so intimately about individuals that he could not possibly have known. His book, in other words, was factual in the main, based on published accounts of the lives and discoveries of the scientists about whom he wrote. But large portions of descriptive material in the book are re-creations, speculations from the author's vivid imagination.

The alternative approach is a highly journalistic one, based primarily upon interviews with the subjects and other journalistic research. De Kruif, of course, had no choice in the matter, since his Microbe Hunters were all dead at the time of his writing. However, given the choice of writing about those of here and now or those of the past, I chose the former. Indeed, Sidney Farber, the Boston physician who pioneered using chemicals to successfully treat various forms of cancer, was one of my original choices for inclusion in this book. Another would-be Life Giver was Virginia Apgar, whose "Apgar Score" gave physicians a sound method to evaluate the health of newborn babies and to determine when they need help to remain viable. "Every baby born in the world today," experts say, "is first seen through the eyes of Virginia Apgar."

But both Farber and Apgar are dead, the latter dying in Manhattan within a week of the time I phoned her office inquiring about an interview. Being dead, of course, should not preclude being written about. But even after interviews with several of Apgar's close friends and colleagues, and readings about her life and work, I found it impossible to write about her in the same way I wrote about those with whom I had spent considerable time. And so, in fairness, her story was omitted.

I am under no misapprehension that the narratives contained in this book are definitive, objective histories. They are, mainly, attempts to introduce the reader to the fascinating stories behind some of the major medical discoveries of our time. In his book *Conversations with Kennedy,* Ben Bradlee, executive editor of the *Washington Post,* noted: "Journalism is just the first rough draft of history . . . journalists never could know the whole truth right away. The whole truth takes too long to emerge, and it consists of too many strands for a single journalist to catch in the single sitting that daily journalism demands."

To be sure, the pages you hold in your hands represent more than a single sitting of daily journalism. Time for added research and reflections has been added. But at a time when all of the primary subjects remain alive, as do many of their colleagues, we are too close to the subject to be able to, as Bradlee says, know the whole truth. We are, for example, too close to polio to discuss its defeat objectively. It is a horrible disease, but as you soon will learn it was not the major killer most believe. Still, anyone who passed those long summer days of "the polio season" at home, indoors, cannot be objective about the elimination of that state of affairs; neither can one who has seen a friend dragging a withered limb or who remembers those days of jubilation just after Salk's vaccine was announced and administered to children.

"There are so many legends," said Jonas Salk when I asked him about one of them. "I just don't pay any attention to them.

"You must stop and recall that I was quite busy, and these stories were not unlike fleas and gnats and flies and mosquitoes. I was very much occupied with what I was doing. I was working on flu and polio for a long time together and carrying a tremendous responsibility, moving forward rapidly; and, therefore, when reporters wanted to know what I had for breakfast, that was not what I was concerned with at the time. Therefore, these were intrusions.

"Your being here is an intrusion too. I allowed myself this indulgence although I assure you I get requests for interviews again and again, but I do nothing about them. I don't know why I said yes to you. It was something about what you want to do that made it clear to me that perhaps I ought to take this time out. But this is very unusual, because even now I have more to do than I have time in which to do it."

Aside from a look at a rather difficult portion of an interview, Salk's statement also gives the reader a look at one scientist's view of the stories surrounding any major discovery. The literature abounds with the little half-truths that Norman Mailer has dubbed "factoids"; the author has tried to chase them away whenever possible.

"For better or worse," observes Rae Goodell, "a habit in the news media [is] to emphasize drama and conflict, and to highlight the controversial news stories. If hecklers disrupt a speech, the hecklers, not the speakers, get the headlines."

I have tried to eliminate this practice in *The Life Givers*, hoping instead that the basic stories of each man's career leading up to his major contributions and the stories directly related to them will contain enough drama. For the same reasons, extended discussion of family and home life has been dispensed with, except when especially relevant. After all, the Life Givers are people, just like the rest of us. Perhaps they have at times led more exciting lives because of their fame, wealth, or position. Perhaps they have not. Consider the possibility that such fame and public exposure actually shelter individuals from the joys and frustrations of everyday life instead of intensifying them as many believe. At any rate I have always been a member of the school that believes that unnecessary window peeping—even at celebrities —is mainly meaningless voyeurism.

Some would argue that a more careful study of the physician's personal life would shed greater light on his work. This is probably true to a limited degree, but in a project of limited space it is surely more efficient to get to the heart of the matter and deal with other aspects on a necessity basis. This is the road I have taken; to do otherwise would be to undertake book-length studies of each of the Life Givers.

2 JONAS SALK:
He killed the polio virus

Long before any of the Life Givers were born the great Microbe Hunters of the eighteenth and nineteenth centuries had discovered the connection between germs and disease. This new knowledge paved the way for the first broad successes in controlling dozens of infectious diseases. One of history's cruelest ironies is that those very efforts, grand successes that they were, opened the door for the ravages of the great crippler, poliomyelitis.

Do not, however, be misled. This was no new disease. Biblical references to people with paralyzed limbs probably refer to polio victims. Archaeological evidence points to the existence of polio infections at least as long ago as Egypt's eighteenth dynasty—fourteen centuries before Christ. Even in antiquity the disease struck a personage no less than a high priest of the Temple of Astarte at Memphis. He is depicted in an ancient stone relief with a withered leg. Hippocrates, father of modern medicine, tells of a paralysis that attacked its victims mainly during the late summer and autumn—a period known until very recently as "the polio season."

In ancient times, as today, poliomyelitis was usually a mild viral infection of the intestinal tract—a location from which many of the viruses are excreted. In a less than sanitary society it isn't long before everybody is exposed to the midget microbe. If exposure comes in infancy, all the better, for most babies receive from their mothers a temporary immunity to many diseases, including polio. If a baby is exposed to the virus when it has the benefits of this temporary immunity, it develops a lifelong, active immunity. When a baby goes through this it may suffer a mild illness, but not paralysis. However, if the baby is not exposed to the polio virus within a few months, its temporary immunity is lost. Once this happens an invasion by polio virus can have devastating consequences.

Since most American babies are protected from every speck of dust and dirt, they are not exposed to polio virus in the first six months of life. They have little chance to build up a naturally acquired immunity to polio while still protected. And thus there may be tragedy.

Once the submicroscopic virus particles in the intestinal canal enter the bloodstream they are carried to all parts of the body. Then these "innocent" bits of genetic material invade nerve cells in the spinal cord and damage or destroy them. The result: polio's paralytic signs occur.

The first recorded polio epidemic seems to have taken place in England in 1835. Six years later came the first United States epidemic in Louisiana. What epidemics these were. Four cases of polio in England and ten in Louisiana. Yet polio frightened tens of millions because of its dread paralysis, but the disease never really ravaged mankind. Even in 1952, the last big epidemic year, there were 57,879 cases in the United States—367.4 cases of polio per million population. What is that compared to the influenza epidemic of 1918–1919 that killed more than twenty million worldwide; or the scourges of cholera and yellow fever; or the Black Death of the Middle Ages when entire communities were wiped out?

One may rightly ask, why all the fuss about polio, also

known as infantile paralysis? Within the answer lies the key to this story of a handful of unusual men and women, as well as millions of ordinary citizens. Together they composed an episode unique in the history of medicine. It did not happen because polio was one of the great killers of mankind, but rather because polio, perhaps more than any other disease, is difficult to forget. When plague or cholera struck a nation, thousands died. The survivors mourned, and their lives were empty for a while. But the dead were buried, if not forgotten, and the voids soon filled.

If that had been the way with polio, I would not have had this story to tell, but I do, for a polio epidemic kills only a few of its victims quickly and a few more after much suffering. Most polio victims survive, often for decades, dragging withered limbs as a constant reminder of the virus that attacked their spinal cords. And those are the more fortunate survivors who were able to get up and, although with difficulty, walk away. More than twenty years after the last polio epidemic dozens of human beings still lie in lifesaving metal prisons called iron lungs, upon which they depend for every breath.

Few who have witnessed polio can forget it; little can be done for its victims and, worse yet, the disease often strikes little children and causes the greatest harm in the richest, cleanest, and most civilized countries in the world.

In the summer of 1916 a spectacular polio epidemic arose in the United States. More than twenty-seven thousand people were afflicted; six thousand died. It was worst in New York City, where the polio virus violated innocent bodies like a Hun: two thousand died and the city panicked. Wild, desperate families fled the metropolis in droves. Citizens of some surrounding communities, frightened that the infection would spread to them, took up arms to turn the New Yorkers back.

In 1916 Woodrow Wilson was President of the United States. Thirty-four-year-old Franklin Roosevelt was a promising young politician. Prohibition was not yet a fact of life, and the First World War—America not yet involved—raged in Europe.

That was the year polio first struck hard.

Not many months earlier, two-year-old Jonas Salk, living in a tenement at 106th Street and Madison Avenue in East Harlem, New York, had just spoken his first words: "Dirt, dirt."

Shortly after FDR was defeated as the vice-presidential candidate in the 1920 election he contracted a fever that doctors at first found difficult to diagnose. It was polio; a severe attack and it left Roosevelt paralyzed in both legs. Instead of giving up he became the "politician in a wheelchair," a great world leader—and the perfect living symbol around which a massive campaign against polio could be built.

By 1938 the National Foundation for Infantile Paralysis had been organized. Roosevelt was its leading supporter. The Foundation's aims were to raise money for the relief and treatment of polio victims and to finance research that might someday lead to a polio-preventing vaccine. FDR's longtime friend and law partner Basil O'Connor headed the organization.

The polio fighters whom O'Connor helped to fund in those days were pretty naive about the disease. The biggest piece of polio information available had been discovered in 1908 in Vienna, when a scientific sleuth named Karl Landsteiner established the fact that polio in man was caused by a virus which he found he could transmit to monkeys.

Late in 1935 more significant information came from an established virologist, Peter Olitsky, and a young Polish immigrant with a recent medical degree, Albert Sabin, working at New York's Rockefeller Institute. The two had tried to grow polio virus in a variety of cells taken from a stillborn fetus. When they planted polio virus in cells harvested from the embryonic nervous system, they flourished. But the same viruses floundered and died when sown in cells from kidneys, liver, skin, and other organs.

This experiment seemed to forever dash hopes for a safe vaccine against polio, for it was well known that an injection of foreign nerve cells could give a person encephalitis. Pasteur's rabies vaccine, of course, depended on viruses cultured in nervous tissue. But there was a world of difference between vaccinating the victim of a rabid dog, who had no hope except the Pasteur vaccine, and vaccinating millions of healthy people with a mixture that *might* prevent them from getting a disease—and then might itself be fatal.

Polio researchers didn't get much good news for a full decade after the Sabin-Olitsky experiment was published. In 1946 Harry Weaver, a professor of anatomy, was named director of research for the National Foundation.

Scientists, mind you, aren't crazy about having their research "directed" or "coordinated." Yet that was exactly Weaver's job.

He called a series of meetings of scientists working under Foundation grants. As an observer with no pet theories, perhaps Weaver could help put matters in perspective—for himself, at least.

Weaver, among others, was disturbed, for example, that established virologists clung to the dogma that the polio virus grew only in the nervous system. True, Sabin and Olitsky had pointed in that direction, but nobody had tried again. "Hasn't it been known for decades," these scientists asked, "that the polio virus is most commonly found in the intestines, not the nervous system?"

It was mainly coincidence that just after Weaver became the Foundation's director of research many dogmas of virology and immunology, particularly relating to polio viruses, began to fall. Actually they were being pulled down by a new generation of scientists.

After several years of work Drs. David Bodian, Howard Howe, and Isabel Morgan at Johns Hopkins University, and others, tried to immunize monkeys against different polio viruses. In doing so, they discovered that there seemed to be three distinct types of polio viruses, and each of them stimulated its own infection-fighting antibodies. Thus a monkey (or a person) immune to one or even two types of polio virus could still be killed or crippled by a virus from the third group. This told scientists that successful vaccination against polio would have to protect the individual against all three types of virus—if, indeed, there were *only* three types.

Now the polio fighters had their work cut out for them. Some would have to attack the tedious job of typing all known strains of polio virus to determine just how many types of these cripplers and killers there were.

Harry Weaver had to find and convince a few virologist-immunologists that the routine job of virus typing could be exciting, rewarding work. He successfully interested and commissioned four university laboratories—in California, Kansas, Utah, and Pennsylvania—to classify one hundred strains of polio virus. It took three years and cost $1.37 million, but it got the job done.

The typing program also brought to Weaver's attention a dedicated young scientist recently arrived at the University of Pittsburgh, Jonas Salk, M.D.

Born into a Manhattan orthodox Jewish family in 1914, Jonas was the eldest of three sons of Daniel and Dora Salk. Daniel was a garment center worker who had designed the detachable lace collars and cuffs that women wore in the 1920s. "He liked to paint and draw," says Salk. "My mother never appreciated that. She was very materialistic. Struggle . . . she knew what struggle meant."

Jonas, neat as a pin and studious, was a perfectionist in school, right down to the last little detail. He wanted to become a lawyer. Dora Salk, however, thought the teaching profession better suited her firstborn son.

"She thought that a lawyer should be very articulate, and with her, I wasn't very articulate. In fact, I tended to stutter and stammer."

Salk didn't like the idea of becoming a teacher but didn't want to go against his mother's wishes altogether. So he considered yet another alternative, medicine.

Jonas committed himself to medicine even though he had no interest in ever setting up an office practice. He liked research. In fact after his first year at medical school he was so committed to this love that he was invited to take a year off to engage in biochemical research. What he learned that year would later add to the sophistication of his vaccine work.

The idea of specializing in medical research was not typical of most medical students of the day, particularly those from poor backgrounds, who itched for the independence of private practice. But Jonas never wavered. Years later when asked why he devoted his life to research Salk replied: "Why did Mozart compose music?"

Salk returned to medical school from his biochemistry work in 1936. He had a pragmatic reason: "If the path I chose in research had been blocked to me for one reason or another then I could always practice medicine," he later said. This referred to the possible effects of anti-Semitism on his career.

The year Salk returned to medical school he heard two lectures that seemed curiously contradictory. A professor told his students one day how the deadly bacterial toxin of diphtheria organisms could be rendered harmless by the addition of a formaldehyde solution. The resultant "toxoid" when administered to people gave them a reliable immunity to the disease. In the next lecture he explained to his students that vaccines to immunize against viral disease had to be made of infectious, living virus.

"Why would a harmless preparation of a bacterial toxin work against a bacterial disease and not a killed virus against a disease caused by it?" the student wondered. Although bacterial toxins and viruses are not the same, the human body reacts similarly to all invaders, producing antibodies to fight them off. Salk thought his professors seemed to be teaching unsubstantiated scientific dogma. It bothered him for years.

Meanwhile, as part of two months of elective work during his senior year in medical school, the twenty-four-year-old went to work with Dr. Thomas Francis, Jr., a virologist-immunologist of considerable repute.

The year Salk went to work with Francis they agreed that Salk would study the use of ultraviolet light rays to kill influenza viruses for use as an immunizing agent against the disease. He was searching for a way to kill the viruses so they would not cause disease but could nevertheless produce enough antibodies to develop an immunity to the disease.

In this work young Salk steeped himself in the basics of virology and immunology. All the while he was courting Donna Lindsay, a girl from a socially correct Jewish family, who had a degree in psychology and was now studying at the New York School of Social Work. They were married the day after Jonas graduated from medical school.

From then until March, 1940, when Salk became an intern at Mount Sinai Hospital, the brand-new physician resumed his work with Francis, who managed to obtain a $100-per-month grant for him.

At Mount Sinai, it was said, stable, unruffled Jonas Salk was the best intern in the hospital—"as versatile and promising a physician as any of them and by far the most mature and most reliable," recalled a doctor who was there.

After his internship Salk applied for a residency at the Rockefeller Institute's hospital. It was run by Dr. Thomas

M. Rivers. In a few years Rivers would be very important in Salk's life, but now he offered no encouragement. Salk's application was denied.

It is not mere speculation that anti-Semitism played a role in keeping Salk out of certain jobs. At one research center a scientist reportedly remarked to his colleague who had nominated Salk, "Next thing you'll be bringing niggers in here." Such an attitude was not unusual in those days, when even the most prestigious medical institutions had quotas for Jewish students.

Thirty years later Salk looked back and noted that "If anti-Semitism had not blocked me from some of the things that I had wished to do, I might not have ended up doing what I did. You have to see this in the perspective of history. You must remember that I happen to live in this country because of anti-Semitism, because my parents fled the pogroms in Russia. Yes, anti-Semitism was a kind of adversity, but I look upon adversity as being evocative as well as frustrating. It might have facilitated my career by directing me to other pathways. In other words, adversity can cause another ending, but it can still be a happy ending. On the other hand, this is not to condone anti-Semitism or any other form of prejudice."

But those are the feelings of a Jonas Salk who had already lived through it all. Back in the 1940s, after being denied a residency at Rockefeller, he received a National Research Council fellowship to study virus diseases. (Coincidentally that fellowship was paid for by an organization known as The National Foundation.) Because of the war and the importance of influenza, Salk decided to rejoin his former professor, Francis, who in the meantime had moved to Ann Arbor, Michigan, to head the department of epidemiology at the University of Michigan's new School of Public Health. Francis was continuing his influenza work and was also beginning a study of polio epidemics.

Salk and his wife left their New York City apartment for a rented farmhouse (complete with a wood-burning stove and a victory garden) on the outskirts of the Michigan college town. At a salary of $2,100 a year, Salk took an active part in the work of developing a vaccine against influenza. Remember, that disease had killed 850,000 Americans—including 44,000 soldiers—in the 1918 epidemic, and with the nation again at war the US Army needed to control influenza epidemics.

Francis and Salk continued their earlier studies of killing influenza viruses with ultraviolet light, and also tried a formaldehyde solution called formalin. They wanted to find a way to kill the viruses without destroying their ability to stimulate the body's production of antibodies which would fight off future invaders of the same type, thus producing immunity.

Professor and former student together perfected a formalin-killed virus vaccine that was effective against the two types of influenza virus, A and B. The flu vaccine was successfully tested on soldiers-in-training at American universities. Salk broadened his research following not only viruses and the body's response to them, but their epidemic effects in populations. Salk's name appeared on many papers out of the Ann Arbor laboratories. He was aware of the necessity of getting his name in front of the scientific community, and he sometimes urged Francis to allow his name to be placed first on the work they had done together. Old-fashioned scientific protocols approve of listing the senior investigator's name first, even if he has done little of the work himself. But Jonas made the point that Francis's name already was well known and that he needed the recognition. It was mainly his expertise, however, and not his lobbying ability that helped Salk become widely known as an expert in the immunology and epidemiology of influenza. But independent minds become restless when they are always working under others, and Salk's feelings soon prodded him to take off on his own. He started hunting for another job.

In 1947 the University of Pittsburgh's Medical School was looking for a young scientist to head a virus laboratory. Smoggy Pittsburgh in those days was a grimy industrial city, and the medical school's reputation left a lot to be desired. But when the offer came, Salk accepted a post as associate research professor of bacteriology. Did he know that he would be the only full-time faculty member of the school? Colleagues there couldn't quite understand why he didn't have a private practice (as they had) in addition to his university duties. A strange fellow, that Salk.

With all of Pittsburgh's shortcomings, it also had possibilities. There was little in the way of research money, but Salk would head his own laboratory—however small at first—and satisfy his deep need to direct research.

Not long after he arrived in Pittsburgh, Salk was chosen to participate in the National Foundation's polio virus typing program. It was believed to be unspectacular, plain hard work, a giant bioclerical task which would examine one hundred known strains of polio virus and neatly (it was hoped) file them according to type. Thousands of monkeys were used, the first of an army that would be used in the next ten years for testing polio viruses and vaccines.

It took more than a year to tool up for the big typing project at Pittsburgh. It didn't begin until April, 1949. In the meantime Basil O'Connor was making sure that the public knew the awful details of the damage polio was inflicting and the growing battle against the disease.

The work of typing viruses went quickly, especially since a method faster than those originally prescribed by the Foundation's conservative Virus Typing Committee was developed and adopted by Salk.

The standard, time-consuming method of typing polio viruses went like this: A group of monkeys would be infected with a Type I polio virus. The monkeys that recovered from this infection would be immune to all Type I polio viruses. Next they would be exposed to a virus of unknown type. If the monkey showed immunity to it, the virus had to be a Type I. But if the monkey became infected, it was obvious that the unknown virus belonged to Type II, Type III, or a type as yet unknown. Then the unknown sample would have to be tested further against other monkeys in the same way until its identification was pinpointed.

The method Salk pursued was far simpler: First infect a monkey with an unknown virus. The infection causes a rise in the level of antibody in the animal's blood. Check this antibody by determining which of the three different known virus types it neutralized, and that was the unknown virus type. It was simple. So simple, in fact, that by the end of the first year of the typing program in Salk's laboratory most of the work had been done. Over the next two years the initial work was reconfirmed by the conventional method.

The Pittsburgh laboratory typed seventy-four unknown strains of polio virus. When data from all four of the typing laboratories became available, it was learned that all strains of polio virus tested conformed to one of the three types suspected to include all polio viruses.

During the typing program Salk picked up two important prerequisites for the development of a polio vaccine: a fine assortment of representative strains of all three types of polio virus and a good deal of experience in the immunization of monkeys against polio.

Another prerequisite came, while the virus typing work was still going on, from the Boston laboratory of Dr. John F. Enders, whose scientific curiosity at the time was engaged with the virus that causes mumps. With Thomas Weller and Frederick Robbins, Enders made some major discoveries. First the trio learned that slow, continuous incubation in test tubes was needed to successfully cultivate some viruses.

Second they found that in order to cultivate viruses successfully they had to eliminate bacterial contamination that
spoiled the cultures. Not long before Enders, Weller, and
Robbins began working together, other virologists had used
penicillin to rid tissue cultures of unwanted bacteria. The
three decided to try penicillin and another new antibiotic,
streptomycin, for the first time in culturing viruses.

In March of 1948 they had set up some culture flasks of
human embryonic tissue with the two wonder drugs. They
had inoculated all of the flasks they needed with the mumps
and chicken pox viruses they were studying. A few flasks remained, and instead of throwing them away Enders remembered that he had a culture of polio virus preserved in a
laboratory freezer.

He put some polio virus in a few of the culture flasks containing bits of embryonic skin and muscle tissue. And it grew.
The polio virus grew in the tissue culture—a culture not
made from nervous tissue. And at last the Sabin-Olitsky work
was overturned. It was shown that polio virus could indeed
grow in tissue that was not from the nervous system. As it
happened, the polio virus that Sabin and Olitsky had used was
a black sheep among polio viruses, the only one that would
not grow in nonnervous tissue.

For this discovery Enders, who had once failed miserably
in business as a real estate salesman, received the 1954 Nobel
Prize in Medicine. He insisted he would not accept it unless
his two junior partners shared in the honors.

During his virus typing work Jonas Salk had learned of
Enders's techniques and wanted to equip his laboratory for
culturing viruses this way, but the National Foundation
offered neither funds nor encouragement. Yet Salk "had a
way of doing things anyway," as he recalls, and he personally
raised the necessary funds locally. His staff quickly mastered
the virus culturing methods and they were soon typing polio

viruses that had been grown in their own tissue cultures. Salk also put his staff to work testing various monkey tissues to determine the most useful in which to grow viruses. They settled on the kidney. And as a medium in which to grow cultures of the tissue cells they settled on Medium Number 199. It was a recipe of sixty-two carefully blended ingredients from salt to penicillin that a Toronto scientist had developed for culturing cancer cells.

"I took advantage of every available bit of knowledge and my own intuition and impulses to move forward," says Salk. "It wasn't unlike someone deciding to go on a trip or to go fishing. The first thing you do is get all of the stuff that you need. The most trivial thing is as important as what may be thought of as the most important thing, because it's all part of the gestalt."

By this time almost everything that was needed for this very special scientific trip had been laid out. All that remained was for somebody to pack things up together properly.

At the Pearl River, New Jersey, laboratories of the Lederle Division of the American Cyanamid Company, one of the largest pharmaceutical firms in the world, Herald Cox and Hilary Koprowski were attempting to tame, but not kill, the various strains of polio virus and use these as a vaccination.

And now established at the University of Cincinnati, virologist Albert Sabin was also convinced that the old live virus vaccine concept was best.

But at the University of Pittsburgh School of Medicine, Jonas Salk stuck to his hypothesis that the killed virus vaccine had to be tried first before giving in to the need for vaccinating humans with living polio virus which might cause the disease.

Salk was too young to be a member of the close-knit community of leading virologists. He was well experienced in the fields of virology and immunology, having successfully worked on the influenza vaccine with Francis at Ann Arbor and later on his own at Pittsburgh. But with regard to the polio research he was a new kid on the block.

It will come as a surprise to many readers that scientists react to such situations the same way as most ordinary people. When a new child comes into a school for the first time, members of the existing group size him up. A certain amount of hazing goes on. Even though scientists are caricatured as idealists they act the same way.

Salk explains the reaction: "If you have a healthy, vigorous desire to do something in a field of science, particularly if you are an outsider, and if you introduce new ideas and methods or discover something new, you are going to be greeted with a series of reactions that can be described as follows:

"Number one: 'It isn't true.'

"Second is: 'Well, if it is true, it isn't very important.'

"Third is: 'We knew it all along.'

"That is simply the way people behave. One has to expect it and if you're fragile, soft, or squeamish, then you collapse and go off and do inconsequential things or you do what everybody else is doing. But if you are by nature an innovator then you have to accept all the difficulties and problems associated with it."

He was brash and young, with new ideas that the established polio fighters sometimes scoffed at. But he had the background, training, and skills, and he was building a sound staff at his Pittsburgh laboratories. Salk thought big. Some scientists are plodders. They prefer to work alone or with an associate and a technician or two, puttering over this or that on a cluttered laboratory bench. Some can work no other way. Jonas Salk, on the other hand, was perfectly comfortable with the idea of using thousands of monkeys and running a staff that would perform many experiments at a time. Salk surrounded himself by able associates such as Dr. Julius Youngner, Major Byron L. Bennett, and Elsie Ward. At the outset they were fiercely loyal and dedicated, but as Jonas moved to bring his ideas to fruition they seemed to drift apart. His increased workload put more pressures on his colleagues, and they felt it. Some later took to calling him—but never to his face—"Jonas E. Christ." Salk signed his paper on immunization of human subjects against polio "By Jonas E. Salk, with the collaboration of . . ." instead of "By Jonas E. Salk and . . ." This didn't help morale a lot. To the very end of the polio vaccine work, however, it can be said that jealousy meant very little when there was work to be done.

Salk had given his first major report on polio research at the Second International Poliomyelitis Congress on September 7, 1951, in Copenhagen. As spokesman for the four laboratories that participated in the Virus Typing Program, he confirmed early suspicions that there were only three types of polio virus. "The task has been accomplished. . . . The consequences that will follow are self-evident," he reported to the group consisting of everybody who was anybody in polio research.

At this time there was another puzzling question that needed to be answered: Did the polio virus spend any time in the bloodstream of its victims? It was generally "accepted" that the polio virus entered the body through the mouth or the intestinal tract and made its way along the nerve fibers to the critical nerve cells in the spinal cord, thus bypassing the bloodstream altogether.

If true, this presented a significant problem. For if the virus never entered the bloodstream, how could a vaccine ever be effective, since a vaccine depends on producing virus-killing antibodies in the bloodstream?

It was a pesky question, since all but two isolated attempts had failed to find any of the viruses in people's blood during polio seasons.

Then in 1952 two scientists working independently at two different laboratories shed new light on the matter. Dr.

Dorothy M. Horstmann at Yale and Dr. David Bodian at Johns Hopkins recovered virus from the blood of humans and monkeys after they had been infected with polio viruses. And finally it was clear that the polio virus was not transmitted through nerves as was believed true for the rabies virus.

The sneaky polio virus had been so difficult to catch in the bloodstream, because it lurked there only a day or two before invading the nervous system. The polio fighters were excited. Now they knew that enough antibodies could intercept and attack the invading viruses and thus protect people against paralytic polio.

More indirect evidence supporting the fact that polio could be attacked in the bloodstream came from Dr. William Mc-Dowell Hammon, a colleague of Salk's at the University of Pittsburgh School of Public Health. Hammon showed that gamma globulin, a blood derivative that contains antibodies produced by natural infection, could temporarily protect against polio paralysis when given at the proper time just before exposure to the virus. It was only a limited weapon, for the product was too scarce and too costly to be given except to those under immediate and direct threat of infection. By this time, however, the public wanted to try anything to prevent polio, and Basil O'Connor felt obliged to have the National Foundation buy the entire national supply of gamma globulin to keep it in reserve and available for epidemic control.

Jonas Salk wasn't sitting around waiting for each of these developments before he began to work on a vaccine. In early October, 1951, when he returned from the Copenhagen conference, he used data and techniques already at hand to begin polio immunization studies on mice.

Salk is a man obsessed with reason and order. He neatly classifies his thoughts instantly, and speaks in organized sentences and orderly paragraphs. True, he did not pursue his first love, the law. Perhaps it was the same drive that instead stirred his interest in the laws of nature.

"Whenever something is possible," Salk reasons, "there are conditions under which it is not possible. If it is ever said that something is not possible, then one has to examine to see whether there are any conditions under which it is possible. I was interested in determining whether something might work and I approached this by trying to disprove my hypothesis. And if it resisted the effort to disprove it, then it withstood the test. If on the other hand we demonstrated that it was possible, then we had shown that there are times when it works. We need to establish the parameters within which it does work and then find the degrees of freedom and the requirements for something to be reproduced repeatedly and consistently."

Salk, you will recall, was no neophyte scientist. He had had years of experience in the epidemiology of viral disease, especially influenza. When he sat alone in his office, feet propped on the edge of his desk, he could not imagine "how one could possibly test live virus vaccines in the human population without running the risk of causing paralytic polio. It was an ethical question that was inescapable. From the outset this became a very strong and compelling factor in my determination to study the possibility of developing a killed virus vaccine."

Salk also stresses, however, that he "was interested in understanding the nature of the disease process and the nature of the mechanism of the immunization process." He was disturbed by those who kept referring to him as a product developer. "I always resented people who kept asking 'Do you have a vaccine?' especially when I kept insisting that this would be a by-product of the studies on the possibility of inducing immunity with killed virus preparations. I was attempting to understand the nature of the process to determine whether or not this could be done."

This is often a difficult concept for nonscientists to comprehend. We simply assume that dedicated scientists know what they want to discover and set out after it. Certainly research is directed to some extent, but not as much as we usually believe. It brings to mind my own experience with a college zoology professor whom I particularly admired. He once showed me the laboratory where he pursued his studies of the organism that causes malaria. "Oh," said I, "you are finding a cure for malaria." Somewhat puzzled by my conclusion he quietly explained, "No, I'm just studying the malaria organism to learn more about it."

Similarly, explains Salk of his polio work, "There was both an intellectual challenge and a result that would have clinical significance. . . . This combination of a scientific worker and a product developer was most unusual. It happened because of the unique nature of the given situation, but it was not planned or plotted or looked forward to, nor could it have been."

As he and Francis had done with influenza viruses, Salk began to use formalin to kill polio viruses. He concluded that he had to dissociate the infectious components from the immunizing components of the polio virus.

"That was a very basic concept for me. The basic idea is that the virus has both the capacity to infect and the capacity to immunize. If it was possible to destroy the infectious capacity without destroying the immunizing capacity, you would have a noninfectious vaccine; you then don't have to worry about whether an attenuated live virus [used in the oral vaccine] will revert to a virulent phase or not."

So Salk experimented until he found just the right conditions for killing polio viruses without diminishing their ability to incite antibody production.

"The method," he explained to a reporter at the time, "is very much like the one a housewife uses when she wants to prepare a new dessert, say a cake. She starts with an idea and certain ingredients and then experiments, a little more of this and a little less of that, and keeps changing things until finally she has a good recipe. In the process, she will have deduced certain universal laws which govern such things. From there she can go on to make further improvements during the years."

Even though heat was not actually involved, the virus killing method was commonly referred to as "cooking." In fact the virus-containing fluid was exposed to formalin at body temperature. After the virus had steeped in the formalin for a specified period, the resultant material would stimulate antibody formation in monkeys, but was not infectious.

Salk's theory about inactivating viruses met with great criticism in the scientific community. Many scientists argued that one could never be absolutely certain that a given batch of killed virus was 100 percent free of infectious particles. These scientists argued that the only way to be sure of the safety of such a preparation would be to test every cubic centimeter of the stuff by injecting it into monkeys and then noting their reactions. The problem with that method, of course, is that there would remain no material to use for vaccination purposes, which, after all, was the desired result.

Jonas Salk based his faith on the laws of nature. He used a graph to tell the story. The graph essentially charted loss of remaining live virus particles as a function of time.

If, for example, Salk started the virus killing process with a preparation of one million live virus particles per cubic centimeter (the size of a dose of the vaccine), he found that after twelve hours of "cooking" there would be one hundred thousand surviving live virus particles. After one day of exposure to the formalin only ten thousand would remain, and after two days only one thousand live virus particles. Salk estimated that by the end of three days there would remain only one of the original million live virus particles per cubic centimeter. If the process was continued for another six days there was only a one-in-a-trillion chance of finding a live virus particle in a single dose. Hence, a "margin of safety." Salk concluded: "The material treated for a total of nine days or longer should, theoretically, be free of any demonstratable virus—even if all of the fluid being converted into vaccine were tested in tissue culture or even in man."

Salk had to have faith in the laws of nature, for there was simply no way he could fully test his hypothesis. He could only go so far, then he had to depend on the consistencies of nature. "If it were merely haphazard, it would be contrary to the way things function in nature," Salk reasoned. And when reporters asked him how safe his vaccine might be he said, "There is no question of 'how safe is it?' It is safe, and it can't be safer than safe."

Now any successful process of immunization against polio would have to cause the body to produce antibodies against all three types of polio virus. So Salk had to choose the best strains of each virus type to use in the vaccine. The most important was Type I, since it was the most common cause of paralytic polio. Choice of the strain was to be made on the basis of its efficacy to immunize when made into a vaccine. Since Salk was perfectly confident of his ability to kill the virus he didn't think safety was really a problem. So the strain that would give the best immunity was most important. He worked with a Type I strain called the Mahoney strain, isolated by Dr. Francis from a family in Ohio. For his Type II strain Salk chose MEF, which had been isolated from an adult in the Middle East Forces during World War II, and for Type III he chose the Saukett strain, which had been isolated in his own laboratory in 1950. The Saukett strain had been obtained from the stool specimen of a paralyzed boy named James Sarkett. But a technician's sloppy handwriting on a flask was read "Saukett" and so it was written in medical history.

Salk grew the three types of viruses in cultures of monkey tissue according to methods modified from John Enders's techniques. He nourished them in mixture 199 and harvested them by whirling the concoctions in a centrifuge. Then he killed the viruses according to his margin-of-safety technique and tried the vaccine on animals.

It worked. The monkeys did not get sick or die. The levels of antibodies in their blood went up, and they successfully resisted challenge with live, virulent polio viruses. A killed virus vaccine had immunized the monkeys against polio. Salk also suspended the polio virus in a mineral oil emulsion for injection to enhance the immunizing effect by holding the dead virus at the site of injection and releasing it a little at a time. But there was considerable criticism over use of the oil medium. Some claimed it might cause too much inflammation and others said it might eventually cause cancer. Salk soon dropped the oil idea to avoid further controversy.

More and more monkeys were vaccinated and tested, and by June of 1952, Salk was satisfied that he could begin tests in humans. But testing in monkeys was a long way from testing in people. How could he test the safety and efficacy of his vaccine in people without exposing them to danger—and without undue publicity that might falsely raise the hopes of a nation in the midst of yet another polio season?

He found the answer after consulting with staff and the board of trustees at the D. T. Watson Home for Crippled Children at Leetsdale, Pennsylvania, fifteen miles northwest of Pittsburgh. Here, with approval of the Foundation and the families of patients, Salk shot his dead polio viruses into children and adults who had already had paralytic polio and thus were immune to whichever type of polio virus had caused their paralysis. These injections could not harm the patients, but a good vaccine would still raise their blood level of infection-fighting antibodies. Salk took blood samples from each child to type the antibodies present from the original infection. Then he injected dead viruses of the same type into each patient. He had taken every possible precaution.

The tests were successful. The children who had been injected showed a significant rise in antibodies, and none became ill.

Lucile Cochran, administrator of the Watson Home, remembers Salk as "not just a scientist on an experiment but a man deeply concerned about the human importance of the experiment. . . . We were all very much in favor of trying it. It may seem peculiar, but we had no sense of making history."

For years prior to the Watson Home experiments studies had been performed on thousands of monkeys in the laboratory. Salk left the handling and even the injecting of these monkeys to his staff specialists, who were far more skilled than he in such matters.

After all, Salk considers himself a "clinical investigator" and not strictly a laboratory man. "Somebody had to orchestrate. Somebody had to sit back and think of the overall. I had to think about all aspects of the very complex problems which required someone to organize, to conceive of the elements that were necessary, to take advantage of opportunities."

But now that matters had passed from the stage of animal experimentation and a giant step had to be taken to real live people Jonas Salk "was not going to ask anyone else to take the responsibility. First of all I was a physician. I was licensed to practice medicine. The technicians helped draw blood samples, but I did all the injecting at that time. I injected the first five thousand. I did it myself. When it was found to be safe then I could ask other physicians to be of help. It had passed the experimental stage."

Salk never seriously doubted that a killed virus vaccine would be effective. Each bit of scientific evidence he had built upon was shown to be true through his continuous probing. Nevertheless, as one might expect, he had all of the nagging concerns anyone would associate with walking a tightrope. "When you inoculate children with a polio vaccine," he was quoted as saying, "you don't sleep well for two or three months."

Just as significantly, at the time, he also said, "I had the courage of my convictions. I couldn't have done it unless I had been more critical of myself than others were of me. It was courage based on confidence, not daring, and it was confidence based on experience."

By the end of 1952 Salk had injected ninety-eight patients at the Watson Home and sixty-three at Polk State School, Polk, Pennsylvania, where he inoculated children with no history of polio and no blood antibodies against polio.

These children also remained healthy after their injections. Salk tested their immunity by taking blood samples. He tested them for virus killing antibodies, which he found in abundance.

Success seemed near and a confident Jonas Salk went to a closed scientific meeting called by the National Foundation and held in Hershey, Pennsylvania, in January, 1953, to report on his work.

The meeting was a quiet one. No newspaper reporters were present to hear the thirty-eight-year-old researcher—who had been working on a vaccine for two years and had only been involved in polio research for five years—tell the nation's polio specialists that he had injected 161 people with experimental vaccines against polio. Actually Salk carefully avoided referring to his development as a "vaccine" and called it an "inactivated preparation."

No music played. He was not heralded as a great scientist. Profuse thanks and tributes were not dumped on the doorstep of the handsome young doctor.

Salk reported that his studies seemed successful; although

there was much more to be done, and he was not yet ready for large trials.

The scientists present, according to Tom Rivers, "put Jonas through his paces. . . . They examined Jonas closely —that's not surprising. These boys would have questioned their own mothers if they were foolhardy enough to give a paper at a conference."

A special stickler in the crowd was none other than Albert Sabin. "Sabin's interpretations," said Salk, "made my work seem of no meaning or significance. We hadn't done this, we hadn't done that, and this was premature, and that was unsubstantiated. I remember asking him later, 'Why do you constantly emphasize the negative?' He answered that this was 'the scientific way of doing things.' "

Sabin was tough, all right. Back in Cincinnati his staff was busy trying to sufficiently weaken—but not kill—polio viruses so they could be used in a vaccine, so Sabin had his own theories to promote. And as science writer Richard Carter has noted, "In the game of science, as in other competitive pursuits, one may win honor not only by running faster but by maneuvering the other fellow into running slower." That's just what Sabin was doing, and though he retained his many admirers, he was labeled "a nuisance" by others.

Salk's work shone through the tough questions. Basil O'Connor rose and told those gathered that the National Foundation would not interfere with Salk or pressure him to move faster. But, O'Connor added, if and when Salk was ready for large-scale testing of his "inactivated preparation," it would be his "obligation as an individual and a physician to move ahead."

In March, Salk's report appeared in the *Journal of the American Medical Association,* titled "Studies in Human Subjects on Active Immunization Against Poliomyelitis."

And a public that had been chipping in its dimes for years

began to get even more excited about what was going on in the laboratories of the man reporters were starting to call "a real-life Kildare."

A few days after the Hershey meeting, somebody leaked word to syndicated columnist Earl Wilson that there was a polio vaccine. He wrote a story headlined "NEW POLIO VACCINE—BIG HOPES SEEN." At about the same time the National Foundation held a dinner to which the press had been invited and said that there had been "tremendous progress" in the development of a polio vaccine.

By this time there was already "too damn much excitement" for Salk, who was deeply disturbed by the publicity and felt he was responsible for seeing that no false hopes were raised. So he went to New York to confer with O'Connor and Foundation Research Director Harry Weaver. Claims being made in the media should be toned down, Salk argued. "I'd better go to the public myself and try to set the pitch at middle C instead of high C."

A radio appearance and press conference were arranged so that the polio virus killer himself would talk directly to the people on the same date that the AMA *Journal* would publish his first article on the "inactivated preparation." He didn't want any sensationalized versions released by overeager reporters.

At this time Salk clearly had not become used to being the celebrity, and the press, television, and radio interviews were rough on him. In these appearances he was always the scientist, self-assured, impeccably neat, but most of all he was cautious and deeply private. He resented the intrusions into his personal life, which he firmly refused to discuss. "Why do they want to know what I have for breakfast?" he once asked a friend.

Salk was deeply hurt when, instead of applauding his caution, many fellow scientists lambasted him for not confining his reports to the scientific journals. One scientist reportedly said to Salk at this time, "Well, Jonas, the only time I see you these days is on television."

Meanwhile, without much publicity, Salk was extending his tests in the Pittsburgh area. He continued to give all of the injections himself. At a typical school the youngsters lined up to enter the room where Salk waited while his secretary Loraine Friedman handed each of them a test tube bearing the child's name and control numbers.

Softly she answered questions about what would happen, and along the line nurses deftly withdrew tubes of blood from the thin purple veins in each child's arm.

The other arm was swabbed with a cotton ball soaked in alcohol and Salk hurried over with a hypodermic syringe. Quickly he jabbed the needle and injected a single cubic centimeter of vaccine. The children grimaced, "ouched," and marched bravely into another room where a nurse watched their reactions. The most common: "I didn't even cry."

Just because Salk went into research didn't mean that he didn't know how to handle patients—especially young ones. Almost every child got a smile and warm word from the doctor, and he easily calmed some who screamed with fright.

Instead of facing crying scenes with his own youngsters, Salk injected them while they slept. His three sons, his wife, and other National Foundation families were among the 434 subjects who were vaccinated in the three months after his *JAMA* paper was published. (Salk had injected a dose of the vaccine into himself months earlier, during the first stages of testing.)

He worked eighteen hours a day, sometimes more. "As a medical scientist," he has said, "I've had training and opportunities beyond those of many other people. I feel an obligation to use them for socially useful ends." Salk knew that he was still involved in a "scientific" research project and not a polio prevention campaign, but the fact was that in 1953 polio would kill more children than any other communicable disease.

Jonas Salk was preoccupied with his work. Faint memories of golf and tennis barely lingered. One day while sitting at home with his wife, who was talking about some family matter or another, she noticed that his thoughts were back in the laboratory. "Why, Jonas," she protested, "you're not listening to me at all."

"My dear," Salk grinned in reply. "I'm giving you my undevoted attention."

Jonas Salk, the people said, was "hurrying slowly" toward his goal. And he told Basil O'Connor that he would not significantly expand his testing without the approval of a neutral committee.

By spring, 1953, a Vaccine Advisory Committee headed by Dr. Thomas Rivers of the Rockefeller Institute was formed to study the matter and decide whether to recommend a mass trial of the polio vaccine for the entire country. They decided that if the small-scale testing continued without a major hitch, 1954 should be the year.

At this time, reported medical writer Vic Cohen, Salk, Rivers, O'Connor, and their associates were "becoming the target of much scientific and medical criticism, and some plain backbiting."

At the center of the controversy, as it had been for the past three or four years, was the nagging belief among many scientists that only live-virus vaccine could be effective. "Voodoo superstition," snapped Salk. He stressed, however, that the first injection of vaccine would produce only a small amount of antibody, but it would alert the body and prepare it to make a large and powerful supply of antibodies upon receipt of a booster shot.

In September, 1954, Salk told the Third International Poliomyelitis Conference in Rome:

"Those who believe that living-virus vaccines present the

only satisfactory means for immunization say that there is no immunity like convalescent immunity. We faced this issue for ourselves several years ago and proceeded to go both ways at once until such time as we could determine whether or not the immunizing effect of the living virus might possibly be stimulated by a nonviable preparation. . . . Work in our laboratory on the development of an attenuated living virus was continued up to the time it was shown in human subjects that serologic responses that accompany recovery from natural infection could be simulated by the injection of a noninfectious virus preparation. Even though the actual determination that a noninfectious vaccine could prevent paralysis in children has yet to be made, further studies in our laboratory on the development of an attenuated virus vaccine have been postponed."

However, Hilary Koprowski, the live virus man from Lederle Laboratories, told the same audience, "We are living in the era of the live virus vaccine. What we want is to elicit as nearly as possible all the latent capacities of human talent to apply principles, established by Jenner, Pasteur, and Theiler, to the field of poliomyelitis."

Thus Koprowski fanned the ideological fires by invoking the names of the three Microbe Hunters who had successfully vaccinated against smallpox, rabies, and yellow fever.

Episodes like this one made Salk feel like an outsider. "I would walk down a corridor and people would stop talking as I approached. . . . Minds were already made up. What had once been skepticism about attempts to develop an effective killed vaccine was now becoming an ideological conflict. It was developing into a war against the killed vaccine principle waged by persons devoutly unable to reconcile themselves to its heresies, which were my heresies. How dare I claim that the world is round, not flat."

However frustrating things became, though, Salk rarely lost his temper in public. He would, instead, often retire to his room and put his feelings into writing as a letter or a speech. His anger thus vented, he threw away the draft and went to sleep.

Salk was not without his supporters during all this, and one of the most valuable of them was not a scientist but the powerful Basil O'Connor, who developed a kind of father-son relationship with Salk.

By November, 1953, plans were firm for the national field trial. About half a million second graders were each to get three injections, beginning early in 1954. To check results the disease rate in vaccinated second graders would be compared with the rate in unvaccinated first and third graders. Initially, before Francis accepted the responsibility for conducting the field trial, Salk had favored this type of a "control" rather than the classic "placebo" control where half the population in the study would be injected with an inert preparation while others received the real vaccine.

Even while vaccine production for the field trial had begun controversy over Salk and his techniques continued to rage. Dr. Albert Milzer at Chicago's Michael Reese Hospital reported that he kept getting live viruses in the vaccine when he prepared it according to Salk's recipe. Salk supporters insisted that Milzer wasn't using the method correctly and that Salk's method produced safe vaccine.

Now two pharmaceutical firms had been signed up to make the vaccine. They followed Salk's directions but on a larger scale. Live virus showed up in the first batch of the vaccine because of failure to remove all particles from the fluid. Such particles protected the virus from attack by the formaldehyde. In two other cases unexplainable damage was found in monkey spinal cords in the safety tests but was not due to polio virus infection.

Each batch of the Salk vaccine was a "Goddamned research project," according to at least one scientist involved.

"It was," said Salk. "If the pharmaceutical firms couldn't

reproduce our results you could either assume that I was wrong or they were wrong. The prevailing attitude was that I must be wrong. So I had the dual problem of, first, establishing what I did in the first place and the other of explaining the difficulties encountered by others. I had to show that the method was perfectly logical and rational and if they couldn't repeat our work it was because the conditions under which they attempted it were not the same. They might have disregarded our specifications, either because they thought they weren't necessary, or they knew better, or they didn't respect the fact that it is necessary to start from what is known if you wish to go into something that is an improvement."

It was decided that each batch of vaccine would be checked three times. By the laboratory where it was made, by Salk's own laboratory, and by the Federal Laboratory of Biologics Control.

Through the controversy Salk became ever closer to O'Connor, who said that during this time Salk "had to adjust himself to working out in Madison Square Garden with all the floodlights on him. I think he handled himself very well."

With all of the work and preparation for the 1954 field trials, they were almost stopped before they began.

There were those continuing doubts (by almost everyone but Salk) that the vaccine might not be safe, questions about effectiveness, and a broadcast by Walter Winchell (who had been "tipped off" to the controversy by medical writer Paul de Kruif) topped off with the words, "The new polio vaccine may be a killer."

There were delays and changes in procedure. But the big question was who would be the person to evaluate the results of the trial? It had to be someone who had access to staff and facilities. Someone whose expertise in such matters was the very best available.

Now the Foundation made an important move. It persuaded Dr. Thomas Francis, Jr., to evaluate the results of the mass trial. Fond as he was of his former protégé Salk, everybody knew that Francis was no man to be influenced by such emotions or by pressures. He was a scientist above reproach.

Reached by telephone while visiting London, Francis drove a hard bargain. It had to be done his way. He insisted that some children get dummy shots instead of real vaccine to help better evaluate the effect—and nobody would know who got what until Dr. Francis and his assistants decoded the numbers. He demanded that $900,000 for the study be paid to the University of Michigan. And he said that he and his staff would keep all data to themselves until their report was finished. No tidbits of information—encouraging or otherwise—would be leaked in advance.

Now the stage was set for the largest trial of any medication in the history of the world. The discoveries of Edward Jenner or Louis Pasteur had never been tested like this. In 1796, Jenner proved his smallpox vaccine by testing it on one eight-year-old farmboy. Not today. On Monday morning, April 26, 1954, the grade schoolers lined up in armories, auditoriums, and gymnasiums across the country. The first, second, and third graders waited to get stuck in the arm, for the injections of a few drops of cherry-pink liquid.

There were thousands of volunteers, principals, doctors, nurses, and others. One union in a medical supply factory even stopped a strike so enough needles and syringes could be shipped. Hundreds of thousands of parents willingly volunteered their youngsters, knowing full well that some would receive a pink placebo injection, and thus no protection at all. This was a nation's fight against an enemy that had already killed or crippled too many of its children. Everybody wanted to get in on it.

Each child got a lollypop and, for completing the entire series of three injections, a button proclaiming he or she was a "Polio Pioneer." When it was all over 441,131 of them had received real vaccine, 201,229 received placebo, and there were 1,063,951 who received nothing at all and would be watched as another control group.

It was time for millions to wait . . . and wait. Would the next polio season bring more tragedy? Or would parents relax when their children went off to the local pond or swimming pool? Would the iron lung business continue to boom? Or would it bust? Tommy Francis, true to his word, didn't leak even the tiniest smidgen of information from his offices at the University of Michigan.

The success or failure of the polio vaccine was one of the best kept secrets since the Trojan horse. Still, anticipation was high. The Sunday before Francis's report was to be delivered, Dr. Howard Rusk, of whom we will hear more in the next chapter, wrote in his weekly *New York Times* medical column:

"The fight against polio can be compared with a war. Tuesday may bring victory in a major battle—a real 'breakthrough.' Wars, however, are not won by single battles. Much will still remain to be done—further research, continued education of professional personnel, treatment for those who develop the disease because of lack of vaccination, medical care and rehabilitation for those who have already been crippled by the disease."

On Tuesday, April 12, 1955, the eyes of the world were on Ann Arbor, Michigan. Dozens of television cameras and radio microphones were set up outside the University of Michigan's Rackham Building. Inside, a battery of sixteen cameras stretched across a long wooden platform.

And at 10:20 A.M. the director of the Poliomyelitis Vaccine Evaluation Center, Dr. Thomas Francis, Jr., was introduced. Now he would tell the world whether to shout or to weep.

Hidden by the lectern to his breast pocket, the short, chunky Francis looked across his audience of five hundred doctors and scientists. Bathed in spotlights, Francis was the target as the cameras ground away.

Then, reported *The New York Times,* "Dr. Francis adjusted his horn-rimmed glasses and began to read his long-awaited report in a slow, conversational tone. It was the report of a meticulous and dedicated scientist, presented without dramatics.

"He talked for an hour and forty minutes, the audience was quiet and respectful, there were no bursts of applause. Even after his report the applause seemed restrained."

It may have been restrained inside the salmon-colored hall, but outside bedlam reigned. For even the best laid plans for secrecy are subject to failure without cooperation.

Traditionally, advance papers of major speeches by political figures and scientists are released slightly ahead of time to the press to allow them extra time to digest and summarize the material before they file stories.

But things didn't go smoothly for the press that day in Ann Arbor, reported *Editor and Publisher* magazine. "There was wholesale chaos as some 150 newsmen struggled and fought for copies of the report on the success of the 1954 field trials of the vaccine."

At 9:19 the AP's Alton Blakeslee had his first report on the wires in newsrooms across the world: "The Salk vaccine is safe, effective, and potent, it was officially announced today."

It was normal for advances of such major stories to move on the wire, embargoed until a specified time. And everybody —almost everybody—observes the rules. But Dave Garroway of the "Today" show saw the report at it ticked over the AP receiver. "The news was too good to keep," he said, and put the secret on the air an hour before Francis ever got to the podium.

By the time he did, the world was thanking Jonas Salk. Church bells rang, sirens roared, principals went on the PA systems in their schools and made the dramatic announcement. Teachers wept and children cheered. Impromptu signs were posted and painted on windows from Maine to California.

And if all this irked the press, how is one to describe the disgust of the scientists, secretive fellows who preferred such studies to be published first in their esoteric journals and only later seeped, bit by bit, to the public.

Salk was stuck in the middle. And although when he took the podium at Ann Arbor he received a thunderous ovation from the scientists and doctors gathered, the fact was that they were already blaming him even though his personal distaste for the commotion and publicity was well known.

Here is what the Francis report said:

—The Salk vaccine was effective in the majority of cases. It was found to be 70 percent effective in the placebo areas and 62 percent effective in the observed control areas. Against spinal paralysis the vaccine was 60 percent effective and it was 94 percent effective against the devastating bulbar paralysis type of polio.

—The vaccine's effectiveness varied for different types of polio. It was least effective against Type I.

—The effectiveness of the vaccine varied from batch to batch; some batches were not effective.

—The vaccine did not prevent the nonparalytic type of polio. This was an advantage since the nonparalytic polio doesn't do any permanent harm and gives its victims natural immunity against paralytic polio.

—There was no evidence at all of any danger from the vaccine.

Now there was a great controversy over these results. It did not occur because of Francis's brilliant study, which quickly became a permanent classic in epidemiology. Controversy arose because of the press releases issued by the University of Michigan Information Office. Some thought they were overly optimistic stating, first of all, that "the Salk vaccine had proved to be up to 80 to 90 percent effective in preventing paralytic polio."

Sure, the vaccine worked. But how well? In some of their follow-up stories a few reporters began to hedge their bets, falling away from total faith in the vaccine's infallibility. But these stories came in the wake of the wave of optimism and they didn't affect the public's joy. In fact, if a person knew what to look for in the Francis report, much more optimistic facts could be found.

One of the few laymen capable of deciphering these was science writer John Troan of the Pittsburgh *Press*. A Salk intimate, Troan looked at the report seeking the same type of information Salk would. And he wrote for his newspaper:

". . . a detailed study of the Francis report shows that the 'good' batches of vaccine . . . were more than 94 percent effective against Type I crippling.

"For instance, in the 'placebo areas,' where half of the children got dummy shots, 84,000 nonvaccinated children were crippled by this same virus.

"In other areas, where no dummy injections were given, the 'good' vaccine batted a perfect 100 percent against the Type I virus. . . . Thus, only if Dr. Francis had counted the 'good' vaccine and had ruled out the stuff whose strength was listed as moderate, low moderate, or poor, the Salk antipolio weapon would have rated even better than '80 or 90 percent effective' in preventing paralysis."

After Francis's report, Salk climbed to the podium to deliver a paper. "It is not gambling in which we have been engaged, but rather in pursuits in a field of science," he said to critics.

He reported that new studies showed that the potency of some of the field trial vaccines was low because of the Merthiolate that was added to prevent bacterial contamination in the vial. Salk had insisted it wasn't necessary. The statistics showed that it destroyed potency. Merthiolate had since been eliminated from the commercial vaccines that were being produced and bottled even as Francis and Salk spoke. (Weeks before, Basil O'Connor had staked several million dollars on his bet that the Salk vaccine worked, and he assigned contracts for commercial production.)

Wanting to waste no time, and while he had the world's undivided attention, Salk recommended a new dosage schedule—the first two shots a month apart and the third to come seven months later. This, he said, produced the highest degree of protection.

"Theoretically," he added, "the new 1955 vaccine and vaccination procedures could approximate one hundred percent protection from paralysis."

Now 100 percent is a pretty high number. It is a goal, most scientists will tell you, that is practically unattainable in biology. Even the most effective vaccines—yellow fever, smallpox, tetanus toxoid—are only about 95 percent effective. And by making such a statement on the day of the Francis report, Salk further alienated many of his fellow scientists, including Rivers and Tommy Francis himself. But bright, shining Jonas Salk, with his thick-rimmed glasses and high, dark hairline, did not alienate his fellow Americans or the world.

When Salk was asked in a television interview who owned the patent on his preparation, who would reap the royalties for its manufacture, he replied: "The people. . . . Could you patent the sun?"

They loved this handsome young polio fighter. He was swamped with awards, invitations, and offers of all kinds. Adoring citizens of the world named their children after him and sent him thousands of telegrams and letters. As often as not a gift or token was included: cash, checks, cakes, cookies, scrolls, photos, and good luck charms of every description. Hollywood wanted to make a movie of his life with Marlon Brando in the starring role. President Eisenhower gave him a special citation, and he was awarded a Congressional gold medal. Salk could go nowhere without recognition; autograph hunters hounded him and little old ladies kissed his hand. Simply turning down the requests being made took a staff of several. Salk held a few press conferences but only to talk about the vaccine. His private life remained his own, and that would be that. "I want to get back to my lab. There is more work to be done," he pleaded with the public.

But the accolades continued to rain on him. Universities conferred honorary degrees, great nations dedicated monuments and boulevards to him, he was offered endorsements and get-rich-quick schemes of every kind.

He was nominated for a Nobel prize which, contrary to what many people think, he didn't get. When his name was put before the prestigious National Academy of Sciences for membership, he was turned down. The world was in love with Jonas Salk, but scientists were still scorning him. He was too smug, too comfortable, too aggressive, too handsome, too . . . too right.

Within only seven hours after Francis's report at Ann Arbor, officials in Washington granted licenses to six pharmaceutical firms to manufacture and sell the Salk polio vaccine. Some doom criers forecast panic about vaccine supply, but there was no panic, and the drug companies that had been stockpiling vials of the stuff began to distribute them.

Tragedy descended only two weeks after the Francis report. Word came from Idaho and California that children who had been inoculated with the cherry-colored liquid had come down with polio. The list of casualties continued to grow. Within days the problem was traced to bits of live virus found in a batch of vaccine from the Cutter Laboratories. On May 7, 1955, Surgeon General Leonard Scheele told reporters he thought all polio vaccinations should be suspended temporarily—for a month, perhaps.

Many saw this as strange. After all, there was nothing wrong with the Salk vaccine itself. It was only a few batches that had been manufactured incorrectly by a single pharmaceutical firm.

"Anything was called The Salk Vaccine, whether it had potency or it didn't have potency, so long as it had been treated with formalin properly or not," said a disgusted Salk. "I got the credit for other people's ineptitudes. And Sabin and others were always delighted in talking about The Salk Vaccine and then citing all they thought was wrong, without ever acknowledging what was really wrong."

Nationwide use of the vaccine was officially resumed on May 26, but the damage had been done. A smaller than expected number of children were vaccinated in the summer of 1955, and who knows how many were needlessly paralyzed because they didn't get vaccinated. With time public confidence in the killed virus polio vaccine was restored. By 1958 half of the US population under age forty had been vaccinated and the incidence of polio infections was slashed a full 86 percent from the time before the vaccine was available.

Part of this drop was because of something called the "herd effect," a phenomenon that helps protect even unvaccinated individuals, because the source of polio infection had been drastically reduced.

Meanwhile Albert Sabin kept working on his live polio virus vaccine. He had field-tested his product in the Soviet Union and other countries, where people ate sugar cubes that contained a drop of the vaccine. Neither doctors nor needles were necessary, and this was an attractive advantage to many. Soon things began to happen in the United States. Although by this time the Salk vaccine was in wide use and had been all but totally proven, the Sabin oral polio vaccine was licensed in the United States in 1961.

It caused a political uproar in medical circles, and the

initial controversy over the introduction of the Salk vaccine looked like an after-dinner discussion by comparison.

Soon the Sabin vaccine began to replace Salk's. But according to Salk the "changeover to a live virus vaccine was unnecessary. By 1961 the incidence of polio in the United States had dropped to 7.2 cases per million persons. From 1950 through 1954, there had been an annual average of about 255.5 per million."

But that was that. In the course of the next decade, and about fifteen years after it had been introduced, Jonas Salk's polio vaccine became all but obsolete in the United States.

In 1975, however, it was still widely used in other countries, particularly Sweden and Finland, where it is the only polio vaccine used. World Health Organization statistics show there hasn't been a single case of polio since 1963 in Sweden and 1964 in Finland. But in the United States there continue to be some 20 to 50 cases of polio every year, and many of them, scientists acknowledge, are caused directly or indirectly by the live virus vaccine itself. Between 1961 and 1973 there were 131 cases of vaccine-associated paralytic polio in the United States.

Federal health officials say that Finland and Sweden are special instances, since their populations are smaller, more controlled, and less likely to come into contact with a transient population which might spread disease. In the United States, they say, the oral polio vaccine is far easier to distribute and administer than one that has to be injected.

Salk argues, however, that "convenience was not the question. All other vaccines are administered by injection or by scarification, scratches on the surface of the skin. What really was at issue was a principle: Could a killed virus vaccine eradicate polio, produce the herd effect, and provide long-lasting immunity? The evidence accumulated by 1961 indicated that the answers were yes. What was presumed to be possible only with a live virus vaccine could be accomplished with a killed vaccine, without the risk that is always present when a live vaccine is used."

Salk is well aware that his motives will be misunderstood as he speaks out against the continued use of the live virus vaccine against polio. People will think that he is defending himself against Sabin or defending his "product" against Sabin's.

But this, he says, is "a misconception of the force that drives. A scientific principle was at stake. The world seemed different from the way it was described to me, and I went out to explore and find out for myself."

Because of Salk's explorations, polio has been nearly eliminated from the United States and wiped out totally in other nations. Jonas Salk proved the point that a killed virus vaccine could be very effective indeed against polio.

"I was not the kind of person who was going to be deterred. I always said there was an easier way to make a living than doing what I was doing. I guess it all depends on what you value. Someone once said to me, 'Jonas, people will never forgive you for being right. They forgive you for being wrong.' "

3 HOWARD RUSK:
The advantage to disadvantage

When an automobile accident severed the spinal cord of Brooklyn Dodger great Roy Campanella he became quadriplegic. He was so depressed during his hospitalization that he kept asking nurses if there was "anybody else like me who could even feed himself?" Within a matter of months catcher Campy could not only feed himself and get around in a wheelchair but was working with other newly handicapped, restoring confidence in themselves.

A leading conservative political figure in the United States is shot by a would-be assassin and becomes paraplegic. Yet he remains in his job as Governor of Alabama and George C. Wallace continues to be a perennial presidential candidate.

In Tel Aviv, Israel, a twenty-two-year-old triple amputee (both legs and an arm) victim of his nation's latest war is fitted with artificial limbs. Soon he is driving a car with special controls and walking without even the aid of a cane.

A judge who suffered a severe stroke returns to the bench within a year. A Harvard medical student who becomes a quadriplegic is back in school. A boy who was born with stubs instead of legs is able to walk.

None of these experiences, nor the thousands more like them that occur daily all over the world, are considered miracles anymore. They aren't even that unusual. As recently as the 1940s, though, amputees, paralysis victims, and other profoundly handicapped people had little or no future ahead of them. That's all changed now, and it's largely due to a Missouri doctor named Howard Rusk.

His medical philosophy is best explained through a story he used to tell new doctors on his service during World War II.

"I used to have a friend, a hemorrhoid specialist, who was always busy as hell," Rusk would tell them. "This guy was cutting out hemorrhoids all the time. He had very little time to get to know his patients, but he was pretty safe because he had a good office nurse who always gave him the chart with the name and history of each patient he talked to.

"One time this doctor got caught short, though. A woman was sitting in front of him, and he didn't know her, and the nurse somehow hadn't brought in the chart or file. So the doctor looked at her and said, 'Let's see now, you're . . . you're . . .'

" 'I'm Mrs. Jones, Doctor.'

" 'Oh, yes. Mrs. Jones. Have I seen you before?'

" 'But, Doctor,' said a startled Mrs. Jones, 'you operated on me just last week.'

" 'I did?' said the doctor. 'Let's have a look.'

"So he had Mrs. Jones get up onto the examining table and he spreads her two cheeks apart, slaps her on the fanny, turns her over and says: 'Mrs. Jones. Of course I know you. How's your son at Yale? How's your daughter at Vassar? And how's your husband? He's an accountant, isn't he?' "

By this time the young doctors are waiting for the punch line. Rusk says: "He didn't know that woman. He only knew her from an incision in her ass. And all too often what we're doing is treating the disease and not the patient. You've got a patient who is depending on you. Don't forget it."

Now this philosophy of treating the whole patient and not just the disease did not originate with Rusk. He is one man, however, who is largely responsible for its wide acceptance.

Once as Rusk's plane landed in Seoul, Korea, he was greeted by a swarm of orphan children toting hundreds of signs lettered in two languages.

The English read: "Well Come Doctor Rusk."

In Korean: "Long live Dr. Live Again!"

He earned the nickname in the years since 1942 as he, his associates, and his students helped millions of disabled people once again live useful lives. You see, a person who has a body that is less than whole can still live a whole life, and that's what Howard Rusk has helped his patients prove. Those of us lucky enough to be free of major physical disabilities have learned from Rusk, too, for his other lifelong battle has been against the prejudices that exclude the handicapped from the mainstream of life in this world.

It could easily be shown that Rusk was not the founding father of the field of rehabilitation, what he likes to refer to as medicine's "third phase" after diagnosis and treatment. But nobody would argue the fact that he has been rehabilitation's most successful and best known proponent. He never discovered a vaccination or a cure for a killer disease or pioneered a brilliantly innovative operation. On the other hand Rusk never looked only at his patients' diseased organs or crippled limbs. Instead he considered the entire patient. That was his success. And if he had done nothing more than popularize that concept alone it would qualify him as one of the Life Givers.

In August, 1942, Howard Rusk was forty-one years old. Most men would be well set in the pattern of their life by this age, but it was now that Rusk really began to find out what his life's work would be all about. Until now he had been a respected St. Louis internist with a booming private practice.

"Among his patients," wrote an observer of Rusk's early years, "could be counted the cream of St. Louis society and the leaders of the business world who helped to pay the bills, while some old friends, nurses, and the very poor paid little or nothing at all."

But in 1942 Rusk gave up his lucrative practice and joined the army air corps. He was commissioned as major and ordered to report to the hospital at Jefferson Barracks, a St. Louis army training base dating back to Civil War days.

The switch from plush private medical practice to chief of medical services of a one-thousand-bed hospital posed many problems for Rusk. There was the red tape, of course. And he was intrigued by the public health problems in an area where so many men lived together. It also surprised him to see how the stresses and strains of regimented army life affected otherwise healthy young men.

"Another problem that nagged me constantly," Rusk says, "was one which might not, at first glance, appear very serious. It was how to handle convalescent patients. For the medical service staff in a thousand-bed hospital full of nineteen- and twenty-year-old soldiers, this problem could be very acute. Time was bound to hang heavy on these youngsters as they began to feel better. Bored and restless, the convalescents would get in the way or into mischief. You couldn't blame them. If a man was in the surgical section, for instance, he might be in one ward while his condition was acute, then move to the next ward as he improved, and finally to a ward where he could carry his own trays and get along without much nursing. An effort was made to keep together those who were at the same general level of convalescence, but this wasn't always practical. Often in a ward where there were some very sick patients, you would have others engaging in boisterous horseplay, pushing each other around, wrestling in the aisles. Obviously this posed something of a dilemma."

Rusk spent his first weeks on the job observing the army's way of doing things and getting used to his new medical practice. Word soon came that an inspector from the Surgeon

General's Office in Washington was coming to Jefferson Barracks. The place was ordered spit-shined and polished.

As Rusk and Colonel Hugh Jackson Morgan, the inspector, made their way through the wards, "swarms of these convalescent soldiers, in their purple bathrobes and gray pajamas, kept walking by us," Rusk recalled.

The two doctors agreed this was a shameful waste of time. Rusk knew the convalescents hampered the functioning of his hospital. What he didn't know, but Colonel Morgan told him, was that the air corps, smallest of the service branches, had an average of fifty thousand men in its hospitals every day.

"You may not know it," Morgan said, "but it's touch and go as to which side will win this war. And when there are fifty thousand men out of action every day, do you know what it does to training programs?"

The convalescing soldiers were not only a problem at Jefferson Barracks but at hospitals throughout the nation. Time was being wasted. And if there was anything a nation at war could ill afford to waste, it was the time of its able-bodied young men.

Rusk promised Morgan he would give the problem some thought. Soon he went to work on an idea.

"I reevaluated all of my patients, and in about ninety percent of the cases—if their fevers were down and they looked and felt all right—I simply released them. When I was through that hospital was running so smoothly, I was proud of myself. No more crowds of healthy boys in purple bathrobes getting in the way. Now we could concentrate on caring for the patients who were really sick."

Unfortunately the sweet news soured quickly. Within two days 90 percent of the discharged men were back.

"And they were not goldbricking," said Rusk. "They really needed care. I was embarrassed and chagrined. Once again it had been forcibly brought to my attention that there was a great difference between military and civilian medicine. In military medicine I couldn't tell a patient, 'Go home and take it easy for a week or ten days, then come to see me at my office and I'll tell you when you can go back to work.' In the military either a man was in the hospital or he was out. If he was in, he was a patient; if he was out, he was a soldier. And the men I had discharged, though they had recovered from their illnesses, were simply not yet strong enough for such activity. So I was forced to the conclusion that a man couldn't prepare himself for strenuous training routines by playing blackjack in the hospital sun parlor or listening to his bedside radio. But on the other hand, what else was there to do in a hospital? I didn't have an answer."

Rusk's answer was waiting for him a few days later as he made ward rounds. He stopped to say hello to a soldier with a broken leg and pneumonia. The fellow was so angry he almost refused to talk to Rusk.

"What's the matter with you?" Rusk asked.

"I hate this place," said the young soldier. "I especially hate the orderly in this ward. He did me a dirty trick this morning."

Rusk knew of the often cruel practical jokes encountered in hospitals. He waited for details.

"There was this spider web over my bed," the soldier told him, "and that damned orderly came by with a broom and swept it down."

Not such a dastardly deed, thought Rusk, who said, "We've got to keep the place clean."

"But I can't move," said the patient. "All I can do is lie here looking up at the ceiling, and the one thing I've enjoyed in the last three weeks is watching that spider make her web, catch flies, and have young spiders. That web kept growing bigger and better every day, and now it's gone."

These soldiers could not be released from the hospital, yet they were so bored they had nothing to do but stare at the ceiling for weeks on end. Why not bring a program to them?

"Great idea," said the base commander at Jefferson Barracks. "Go ahead and do it."

Rusk was excited about the project. He requested support personnel.

"Don't know where we'd find any extra men for that sort of program," the base commander said.

No help, no program. Rusk just couldn't do it all himself. Fortunately, not many days later, Rusk met a sympathetic veteran of army red tape who knew how to circumvent the problem: Find a couple of suitable men who are patients in the hospital and assign them to the rehabilitation program. When they recover bring them up before the hospital's Certificate of Disability Discharge Board (of which, conveniently, Rusk was chairman) and find them unfit for military service. They would thus be transferred to the hospital and placed under Rusk's jurisdiction.

Then in another day or two Rusk could call a second meeting of his board and reevaluate the cases of these men. The board would now find them fit to continue their military duties after all.

That's how Rusk got his first two staff members.

"Rusk was considered two things," recalled Al Fleishman, his information officer in the air corps. "First he was an upstart, and second he moved too fast.

"When you're under the command of a full-time military doctor, you just don't move too fast. His life just doesn't have to be that fast. In the army you come to work and you do your job and you get a pension after twenty years of service. Then you go into private practice. But here's this young civilian doctor coming into the army air corps and he's finding work for people to do. He's not satisfied that a guy's lying in bed counting bugs up on the wall."

Rusk and his two newly conscripted assistants started by developing a program of physical conditioning exercises for the convalescents. Since each patient was at a different stage of recovery, they tagged the foot of every bed. No tag meant full exercise program. Red tag, five minutes. Blue tag, fifteen minutes. Green tag, one exercise program a day.

And for the laid-up boys who couldn't do much more than watch the spider lure the fly into her shiny web, Rusk's team got several dozen models of various German, Japanese, British, Russian, and American aircraft and strung them up on a clothesline. Now as the bedridden stared at the ceiling they were studying aircraft identification. Every few minutes the rope was yanked, and each patient had a new group of planes to look at. It was soon learned that after a couple of weeks in that ward, patients had become more skilled at identifying the various aircraft than the soldiers who had taken the regular army course in the subject.

The success of the rather crude program was clear proof that the hospital could be used as sort of a school. In addition to the exercise program, Rusk organized courses in Morse code, military courtesy, camouflage, meteorology, trigonometry, calculus, and American history. Not a single teaching method was overlooked. There were lectures, movies, learning games, and correspondence courses. Within a short time the patients were meeting the challenge of study instead of wiling away hours with pinochle and comic books. And they were returning to their units faster than ever. Patients waiting for disability discharges received special programs that helped make their return to civilian life easier.

The Jefferson Barracks Hospital, Rusk wrote at the time, was "transformed into a combination gymnasium, schoolroom, machine shop and New England town hall."

Some of the hospital's medical officers weren't impressed by the rehabilitation efforts. Gloomily they predicted another wave of quick relapses and injuries. Instead, readmission rates decreased. Rusk's program was restoring broken young men to duty days and weeks ahead of normal expectations. The men, Rusk reported proudly, were "being returned to duty ready for duty."

The fact that these benefits weren't just a figment of some optimist's imagination was driven home by a clinical study on six hundred soldiers with viral pneumonia. At first all of the patients were kept in the same ward, but as they began to recover they were divided into separate convalescent sections. In the first ward there were neither educational nor physical exercise programs. In the second ward there were various types of conditioning exercises which progressed as the patients' strength increased. When all the patients had been cared for and the doctors evaluated the statistics, they found that the men in Ward I were hospitalized for an average of forty-five days and had a recurrence rate of 30 percent. But patients in Ward II could return to their units after thirty-one days in the hospital and their recurrence rate was only 3 percent.

Rusk was once again beginning to think he had found the answer to Colonel Morgan's problem of the millions of wasted man-hours. He drafted a short summary and forwarded it to the Washington office of the Air Surgeon, Gen. David N. W. Grant.

Within days Rusk was sitting in Grant's Pentagon office as the General scrutinized the short memorandum.

"This could be a great program. I want it started in every one of our air force hospitals. And I'm going to order you to Washington to be responsible for it." Grant then issued a directive indicating his complete support for a rehabilitation program.

The new chief of the Army Air Corps Convalescent Training Program had his work cut out for him at the 253 air corps hospitals. Some base medical commanders simply weren't willing to accept Rusk's concepts. Many of the old-time army regulars didn't want to waste time with these newfangled ideas. Conventional medical texts had been good enough up to now, and they were still good enough. Physical medicine and occupational therapy were to be accepted as side issues, but they simply were not integral to the practice of good medicine. Besides, what air corps doctor needed more work?

As Rusk traveled from base to base selling his program, he began to win converts to his approach. Still, one of his associates recalled that "the opposition we got from doctors, the way the program had to be force-fed, was just beyond belief. Rusk thought they would jump at it, but that's not the way it worked." His earlier good reputation as an internist and the results he had to back up his theories no doubt gave considerable help. Nevertheless, it took some powerful persuasion before the concept of treating the whole person gained credibility in the air corps.

Rusk had been forced into all kinds of subtle political maneuvers to get the various generals and colonels to take his advice. He frequently made good use of slight exaggerations of his authorization, not to mention white lies.

Rusk, wrote syndicated columnist Marquis Childs in September, 1944, "must be something of a diplomat as well as a scientist and a specialist."

This entire new program of rehabilitation had been conceived and developed to deal with soldiers who became patients before they ever reached combat. But soon Rusk and his colleagues were faced with another problem, the returning wounded. These men underlined the need for total rehabilitation and not simply reconditioning exercises and occupational therapy.

"Suddenly we were faced with men with broken bodies and, all too often, broken spirits. We concluded that our program was a schoolboy project in the context of what needed to be done for the severely wounded—the amputees (the double, triple, and quadruple amputees), the paraplegics and quadriplegics, the blind, the deaf, the disfigured, the emotionally disturbed. These men would need complete rehabilitation, whatever that might be. I wasn't sure," Rusk says.

It has been said that if a man can build a better mousetrap, the world will beat a path to his door. What they don't say is that a better mousetrap in a world without mice is not a very useful invention. But the time for Howard Rusk's dedication to the rehabilitation of severely injured persons was just right. Over the past few years the development and introduction of penicillin and other lifesaving antibiotic drugs had caused a sudden jump in the number of disabled who needed rehabilitation. Their long-term welfare was now a major consideration. Lives were saved in wholesale proportions, tens of thousands of patients who otherwise would have died of infections lived on, but with disabilities.

"Just exactly what could be done for them?" Rusk wanted to know. "And did the air force have the facilities or the inclination to do as much as possible?"

After some strong doses of Rusk, the answers were offered. And the answers were all yes.

Rusk did almost anything within reason to keep his programs going. Recalls his information officer Al Fleishman, "We borrowed, we stole, hell, we expected to get thrown into the penitentiary. We wanted to get airplane engines. Now how do you get airplane engines for a program that doesn't have manpower listed for it? No M.O. So we stole them. We just got them. We took them from someplace and said, 'Let us have them.' And we expected to get caught. They were only old, used engines, but we wanted to train guys to be mechanics while they were still in the hospital."

Much of Rusk's time was now being spent behind a desk in Washington. He was the administrator of quite a large project. But he was still a people doctor, so he often went out to visit the hospitals.

Those who traveled with Rusk on these inspections say he had a way with words that could change the course of a young man's life.

"How are you doing, soldier?" Rusk asked one young man in an air corps hospital.

"I don't know, Doctor. I can't raise my hand above my shoulder. Look at it."

Rusk looked the injured GI over and said, "Aren't you glad we're winning the war?"

The soldier looked up from his bed at the doctor. He had to be careful what he said. After all, Rusk was now a colonel. "What's that got to do with my bad arm? I'm not going to be any good."

"Oh, yes," said Rusk. "If we don't lose the war you'll never have to stick up your arm like this and salute 'Heil Hitler,' but if you can move your arm up to here there are a lot of things you can do."

It made the soldier think about his situation in a different light.

In another ward, in another city, Rusk approached a soldier with leg wounds. He put his hand on the injuries and said: "How are you doing?"

"I don't know," the depressed soldier replied. "I can't stand up on my toes. I took a bullet right through the ankles."

"That's too bad," said Rusk.

"Pretty damn bad," said the soldier, feeling very sorry for himself.

"Well," said Rusk. "I didn't know you wanted to be a ballet dancer."

"Who in the hell wants to be a ballet dancer?"

"If you don't want to be a ballet dancer, then don't worry about the whole thing," Rusk countered. "You won't ever have to stand on your toes then. Do you see me walking around on my toes?"

No doubt Rusk's deep spiritual beliefs helped him to assist his patients cope so well in the face of adversity. He says that he is sure "there is something beyond life. Otherwise it would be very difficult for me to work in this field, to see such torturing of some people. It seems so unfair. If there were kind of an ever-watchful god, as the Bible says, with his eyes on the sparrow he couldn't be very kind and let these things happen. These beliefs may just be wishful thinking, but it would be hard for me not to have them."

Before long Rusk's rehabilitation concepts were being introduced at air corps hospitals and treatment centers throughout the nation. Early in 1944 the first air corps rehabilitation center, in Pawling, New York, was opened by Rusk; his wife, Glad; and General and Mrs. Hap Arnold, both of whom were Rusk converts to rehabilitation. Arnold was the commanding general of the air corps, and Rusk often told his friends, "What I can't get from General Arnold through the tables of organization, Mrs. Arnold can get from him that night in bed."

Rusk described the Pawling center as a combination hospital, country club, school, farm, vocational training center, resort, and "a little bit of home as well. The discipline was minimal and the program informal. Old regular army people would have shuddered, but fortunately General Arnold didn't have the traditional army man's outlook."

The Pawling center was the first of twelve similar facilities the air corps opened during World War II. Some of the soldiers who were sent to them had physical disabilities from combat duties. Others had psychological disabilities. Many had both.

After having flown a number of missions, many men became what the doctors called hostile aggressives. Explains Rusk: "They wanted to go out and punch some civilian in the nose. They were not easy to manage, but that was exactly why we felt they should be in a center like Pawling, where they could be away from the atmosphere of a hospital or the army and in a community with understanding and sensitivity."

The GIs who came to the twelve centers were the men who had reached their breaking points. Rusk explains that everybody has a point—no matter how brave or stable or strong that person might be—beyond which he cannot go either emotionally or physically.

"How many loads of hod do you think you could carry up a ladder?" he would often ask soldiers. "Maybe one, maybe two, maybe five. Maybe you couldn't even get up the ladder the first time. Does that mean you're no good? No. It just means you can only carry one load of hod. Everybody has a breaking point, so why don't we just quit worrying about what everybody else does and see what you can do?"

When broken men arrived at the centers they saw others— some of whom had been more badly wounded than they were —sitting up, eating, dressing, shaving, walking. When one man sees another man with a similar disability doing all those things, despair often gives way to the challenge. "I'll walk if it's the last thing I do," many said. And they walked. But it was only the first of many things they did.

Once newspaper columnist Marquis Childs visited Pawling. He saw the men working out in the gym. An officer told him, "Mark, we'd like to have you take a look at this guy running around the track."

"What the hell is wrong with him," the newsman wanted to know as he saw the sweatsuited soldier. "I can't run that fast myself."

"Drop your pants, soldier," the officer ordered, and there it was for all to see. The runner was a double amputee. One leg had been removed above the knee, the other just below.

But physical rehabilitation was only part of the program. There was educational retraining, as well as sociological and psychological readjustment. There were even special programs for wives of returning soldiers, who had to make special adjustments of their own.

The staffs of the centers included many disabled veterans who had been trained for the new jobs while they were being rehabilitated.

Few doctors or laymen could have imagined how successful Rusk's programs would be, and by May, 1945, he was able to report that the air corps had provided sixty million man-hours of physical and occupational therapy for military personnel who otherwise might have been sent back to civilian life or would have languished in hospitals and been ignored.

Rehabilitation medicine, Rusk-style, was here.

It wasn't as dramatic as when the apple hit Newton on the head. And it wasn't as romantic as the tale of the spore that wafted into the window of Alex Fleming's laboratory and contaminated his bacterial cultures with a green fuzzy stuff called penicillin. You won't compare Rusk's work with Irving Cooper's fantastic brain probes, or Walton Lillehei's spectacular heart pumps. But just as Jonas Salk had to work in the face of the "voodoo superstition" that his killed virus vaccine wouldn't work, Howard Rusk had to combat the tradition of curing the patient's disease and then forgetting about the patient.

His discovery, or rediscovery, or promotion—call it what you will—of the concept of rehabilitation of the whole patient was not as sudden or as radical a discovery as many others in the field of medicine have been. Howard Rusk was neither a laboratory genius nor a technological virtuoso. He was a medical man, but he was also part politician, part salesman, part promoter. More than anything else, the soft-spoken six-footer was an ambassador to the world. He was the ambassador from the nation of fear and dependence, of maimed bodies and crippled minds. It is not a small nation; even today it has many millions of citizens. Howard Rusk set off to tell their stories to the world. He did. And then the one-time

society doctor from St. Louis pleaded with the world for help.
Presidents, prime ministers, and people by the thousands replied.

There was no hospital in Brookfield, Missouri, on April 9,
1901, so the son of Michael and Augusta Rusk was born in
the family's frame house on the north side of town. The Rusk's
first child had died three years before from childbirth com-
plications. Although baby Howard was weak and jaundiced,
he managed to survive.

Brookfield was a country town of five thousand that had
grown up around the railroad station halfway between Han-
nibal and St. Joseph, Missouri. Michael Rusk, called M. Y.
by friends, was part owner of a furniture store and undertaking establishment. He had stables in the city, and farmland
outside of it. The Rusks were strict parents, and Howard was
a good, old-fashioned country boy. His friends called him
Rusty, not as a description of his hair, which was dark brown,
but as a derivative of his family name.

"We had wonderful times at dances and picnics and sleigh
rides—bobbing for apples and picking berries. When we felt
especially wicked, we smoked corn silk—at least the boys
did."

It was sort of a Huckleberry Finn existence, and true to
that tradition Rusty was little more than an average student
at Brookfield High. Social activities and football were worthy
distractions. Although they had no coach and no uniforms,
the Brookfield High boys were eager football players. Rusty
became a star. He attributes that status as much to stubbornness as to guile. A Kansas City sports writer attended one
game, in which Excelsior Springs thrashed Brookfield. The
score was 60 to 0. Later that year the sports writer nominated
Rusty Rusk as first-string center on the All-Missouri High
School Team. "Rusk played on the worst team I ever saw,
and he took the worst beating I ever saw. For that beating, he
deserves this dubious honor."

Rusty had been knocked flat in every play of the game, he recalled, but he kept getting up for more. It was a trait that would be useful in later years when people rejected his ideas on rehabilitation. He persisted, not only to see his concepts accepted but to oversee the successful raising of millions of dollars for all aspects of rehabilitation.

By early high school Rusk's ingenuity as well as his stubbornness were well established. Each summer he and his best friend Wesley McAffee plotted various successful money-making schemes. Once they bought and managed a small ice-cream parlor. Another year they borrowed money to buy machinery to harvest, dry, and sell blue-grass seed, and yet another summer the boys sold life insurance policies to townsfolk.

By the time Rusty was eleven, Brookfield finally had a hospital of its own. It was an old frame house where doctors took their seriously ill patients to perform crude surgery. The kitchen had been converted into sort of an operating room and there were nine or ten beds in the two-story building. If a patient whose bed was on the second floor had to get up or down the stairs, he was carried in a kitchen chair.

M. Y. Rusk had always wanted to be a doctor, but circumstances never allowed him to pursue this ambition. Now his son had already become passionately interested in medicine. The gangling youth—he was six feet tall and 150 pounds by early high school—became especially close to Thomas Fore, one of the local doctors who took a special liking to him. Rusty gave Fore the same kind of attention the other boys reserved for big-league baseball players.

Rusty gladly became the doctor's helper; he scrubbed the operating room and ran errands. He would drop whatever he was doing if he had a chance to assist in an operation or administer first aid to a patient in pain.

In 1917 a local recruiting sergeant, who had been spinning romantic tales of adventure, encouraged Rusty to enlist in the marines. But his parents weren't convinced that this was the right move for a sixteen-year-old, and they encouraged their son to finish high school. When he graduated in 1919 the war was already over. By this time business was going very well indeed for M. Y. Rusk. He was building his land speculations and savings. So it was no great financial burden to help Howard pursue the medical career he was after. The next fall, in a small, shiny black Ford, Howard set off for the University of Missouri.

In 1920 Columbia, Missouri, was a hell of a town. The sprawling, historic campus was especially alluring to a wealthy —$75-a-month allowance—young doctor to be.

The girls were beautiful, the freshman football team was challenging and the camaraderie of the Phi Delta Theta fraternity house held all the promises that a boy ever expected out of college.

There was something else in the fraternity house that would change the way Howard Rusk was to look at his career in medicine: a crippled houseboy who had lost a leg in an accident.

The houseboy "used to thump around on crutches, trying to do his work, and it was so pathetic to watch that we got together a committee, of which I was chairman, to take up a collection and buy him a leg. I can still see his face when we presented it to him. That leg meant everything to him, but it also meant a lot to me because it made me feel the crucial importance to a handicapped person of something the rest of us took for granted—the ability to walk."

The great postwar depression of 1921 knocked the bottom out of Howard's father's land investment pyramid. He could not meet his financial obligations and sold everything, including his farm holdings, undertaking business, livery stable, and furniture store, to pay his sizeable debts. He kept only his home. The family was so broke that Howard wanted to quit school and start working. His mother quickly dismissed the thought and added that the family would find a way to pay his nominal college tuition fee.

When Howard returned to Columbia for his junior year, which would also be his first year in medical school, things were quite different for him. To make ends meet on his new budget he moved out of the fraternity house and took two jobs. He washed dirty glassware in the medical school's bacteriology laboratory, and at night he walked two miles across town to the Boone County Hospital where he worked as an orderly, taking bedpans to and from patients in exchange for a small room in the basement. He learned all of the tricks of the orderly's trade. "I kept my bedpans on the radiator, so they were always warm. For this, my patients were so grateful they would often tip me a dime or even a quarter. One night a man gave me a whole dollar. It was the biggest amount I ever got, and in those days it meant I could take my girl out to dinner and even have enough left to tip the waiter."

Rusk was in love with slender, black-haired Gladys Houx. At first there hadn't been any romance between the two. They had known each other for three years and frequently met, since they had many mutual friends. During those years Gladys felt nothing special for "that very thin boy with the long legs and the turned-up nose." At the end of their fourth year in college they became engaged. It was a time for more decision making as well, since Missouri had only a two-year medical school, and Rusk had to transfer to another university to complete his medical education. His grades were good enough so he could choose wherever he wanted to study, and at the advice of one of his favorite professors he chose the University of Pennsylvania in Philadelphia.

Gladys, who had majored in social work, moved to New York City and got a job as a caseworker. They weren't together, but were a reasonable distance apart. In exchange for room and board at Penn, Rusk managed his medical fraternity's commissary. To finance occasional weekend meetings in Manhattan, Gladys went without lunches and Rusk sold a pint of his scarce blood for fifty dollars every six weeks or so.

When he graduated from medical school, St. Luke's Hospital in St. Louis accepted Rusk as an intern. But twenty-five dollars a month plus laundry, room, and board wasn't quite enough to solve the financial problems facing the young doctor looking for a way to get married.

Rusk was not only broke, unmarried, and working often twenty hours a day, but these were Prohibition times, and it was illegal to get a relaxing drink with one's friends before dinner. That was one problem, however, that could be solved by a lesson Rusk had learned from a college professor—a little medicinal alcohol siphoned off from the hospital pharmacy's supply into a flat bottle hidden under an intern's white jacket. Doctored up with glycerine and oils of juniper, coriander, and orange, the stuff made quite an acceptable substitute for gin—as long as it was well diluted with a mixer.

The young doctors at St. Luke's, as everywhere, had their hands full with routine laboratory tests, physical examinations, and scrubbing for surgery. There were no antibiotics in 1925, so a majority of patients that had infections died.

Somewhat ironically, medical advances such as the introduction of penicillin and other antibiotics made the need for rehabilitation medicine all the more pressing. For, as Rusk explained, "every time you make a medical advance in a way you compound the felony by keeping people older longer, and they get all of the disabilities that come with an aging population.

"And you keep kids alive with all kinds of birth defects. In the past they would have died and been forgotten. You have to do something for them, because if they get older and you haven't done anything about their disability, they say, 'You kept us alive. For what?' "

Even in 1925, however, patients greatly appreciated a physician who cared about them, and Rusk met that demand. After internship he began private practice as the second assistant to a doctor whose office was already established. He accepted the job with the stipulation that he be allowed to see his own private patients after regular office hours. But soon the after-hours practice had grown so large that Rusk felt the resentment of his senior associate and offered to resign. The doctor wouldn't accept, however, and Rusk stayed through the entire year of the agreement. He left precisely on the final day.

Howard and Glad were married on October 20, 1926, three months after he had gone into private practice. He kept his academic side satisfied by taking on some teaching duties as an instructor at Washington University Medical School, where he taught his students to "Do as I do." Rusk's own practice soon had grown so large that he took in three associates and several auxiliary personnel. On busy days the doctors would see seventy-five or more patients in their office and more on hospital rounds and house calls. There were also a few research projects going at the hospitals—nothing "earth shaking," as Rusk recalled, but they kept up his interest, and he was pleased to have quite a few of his studies published in medical journals.

"We were living comfortably in those days," Rusk says, recalling his five-acre home in an affluent St. Louis suburb. His favorite pastimes were Bourbon Boy and Blue Silver, his horses, which he kept stabled along with his children's two ponies in a white frame barn near his house. Rusk's children learned to ride as soon as they could walk and their proud father liked few things better than to ride with them along quiet wooded trails.

The Rusks had many friends and enjoyed a number of lively parties where Howard himself often led the merriment. Once when a gathering at his home got too staid for his liking he led a goat into the dining room and shocked all but his wife—who had learned to expect almost anything. At other times Rusk entertained guests with satiric imitations of various country characters from his Brookfield childhood.

Far from all play and no work, however, Rusk's reputation as a fine internist continued to spread. He was made associate chief of staff at St. Luke's Hospital and in April, 1937, he became the second physician in the country to pass the tough examinations required for membership in the newly organized American Board of Internal Medicine.

There was little doubt that by the late 1930s Howard Rusk had accomplished a great deal. His office files contained the records of more than four thousand patients, and he was recognized as an excellent diagnostician. His income was more than sixty thousand dollars annually, and his family were comfortable in their suburban home. Still, Rusk recalls these as restless years.

Perhaps he was restless because he had become so involved with the routine of a busy practice. He no longer had time to pursue those medical matters which interested him most. And as is usually the case in a general medical practice, most of Rusk's patients had ailments that were routine, medically speaking. When a patient's ills called for a dose of personal attention Rusk had become too busy to give it. Something had happened. Somewhere along the way a good deal of the challenge had vanished.

At this time, too, the world began to heat up politically. Hitler and Mussolini began their tragic marches into history. Spain was at civil war. Japan had attacked China. Americans, although mainly isolationist since the First World War, knew something had to happen. Now Poland and France had fallen, and Britain was in grave danger. Then early one Sunday morning Japan attacked a sleepy Pearl Harbor, and the United States was again at war.

For many Americans, including Howard Rusk, this was a time to look at themselves and ask, "Am I in the right place?" Rusk wondered who needed him most. Was it his patients, with mainly run-of-the-mill ailments, or the wounded soldiers? The answer wasn't difficult, and Rusk decided that he ought to be in uniform. His commission as a major in the army air corps led him to Jefferson Barracks Hospital and later to the Pentagon.

By the time he left the army in October, 1945, *Newsweek* magazine was saying that Howard Rusk "probably knows more about salvaging sick and wounded humanity than anyone else in the country."

The *Newsweek* story was inspired by the Baruch Committee on Physical Medicine, established two years before by Bernard Baruch to reduce the ranks of the some 23 million civilian Americans who desperately needed physical or vocational rehabilitation because of injury, disease, or psychological problems. Baruch was interested in the field because his father had been one of the old-time specialists in physical medicine. Rusk was named the committee's chief consultant on rehabilitation. But this was no full-time job, and he still had to decide whether he would return to his lucrative St. Louis practice or move to New York, where he felt he would have a better platform from which to spread the word about the great need for rehabilitation services.

Eight or nine months before the war was over Rusk had proposed to the American National Red Cross that the organization take advantage of the momentum it had built during the war to sponsor and coordinate community services for returning veterans. Rusk proposed a concept of one-stop rehabilitation centers for the returning GIs.

But the Red Cross didn't buy Rusk's proposal, which was one of many they had before them. Instead they decided to go into the blood business. However, the presentation on rehabilitation had not gone to waste. One of the Red Cross board members was Arthur Hays Sulzberger, publisher of *The New York Times*. And he asked Rusk to drop by for a visit.

"I completely agree with your viewpoints on this rehabilitation, and I think that a service job needs to be done in public education," Sulzberger said. "What do you plan to do when the war is over?"

"Well," answered the colonel, "you know I had a very large

private practice in St. Louis, but I'm not sure that I want to go back. I think we learned some things in this war that need to be applied to the civilian population of the country as a whole. I think I might want to go and teach these concepts at some university."

"Well," Sulzberger said, "why don't you come to *The New York Times* University? We've got a student in every county in the United States, and if you've got a message I can't think of any better place to get it over than the pages of *The New York Times*."

"I'm no writer; I'm a doctor," Rusk protested.

"I've seen some of the things you have written, and I don't see any problem," answered the publisher.

Rusk explained that most of those writings had been done as cooperative efforts with his associates, particularly Al Fleishman and Jack Taylor, a former high school principal who was a top Rusk aide in Washington.

Sulzberger was agreeable to providing editorial assistance, so Rusk and Taylor went to work for *The Times*.

"Colonel Rusk," the paper announced in November, 1945, "will write on the needs . . . of the millions of servicemen facing readjustment to civilian life." The announcement added that later Rusk would take up matters of the civilian disabled.

Meanwhile Rusk continued his search for a university faculty post. *The Times* would be a fine place from which to spread the gospel of rehabilitation, but a daily newspaper wasn't exactly the best place to get and hold the attention of his medical colleagues. Rusk needed an academic base.

As it happened, Sulzberger was also on the Board of Trustees at Columbia University and was interested in bringing Rusk to Columbia's Medical School to set up a department of rehabilitation medicine.

"Howard," one of his friends advised, "they don't want you at Columbia. You'll run into the same thing you ran into in the navy, the air corps, and the army. Nobody wants you because they don't want you pushing them all the time to do a job."

Indeed, the conservative Columbia University doctors weren't ready for Rusk's new rehabilitation ideas. And they made their feelings clear. At about the same time as the Columbia discussions, however, Dr. Donal Sheehan, acting dean of the New York University College of Medicine, was planning a large new medical center, for which a substantial plot of land had already been acquired. With $250,000 already granted from the Baruch Committee, Sheehan wanted one of the new center's institutes to be devoted to rehabilitation. To begin developing a program, Dr. George Deaver had been transferred from the NYU School of Education to the College of Medicine.

Rusk had first met Deaver during the war, when Deaver was medical director of the New York Institute for Crippled and Disabled. There he was one of the first to teach paraplegics to walk and he developed the concept that the initial phase of rehabilitation should be to train the individual to meet all the manipulative needs of daily living.

Sheehan was devoted to the concept of health "in the total individual" and felt the teaching of the rehabilitation concept should be an integral part of the curriculum of all medical students. In short, it looked as if New York University and Howard Rusk were ripe for each other. Sheehan made an offer, and Rusk accepted.

In April, 1946, the first civilian rehabilitation program was started at Bellevue, the New York City hospital where NYU medical students did their training. It was the first medical school in the world to have a major department in physical medicine and rehabilitation.

Now it was a matter of building staff, gleaning more space, getting general cooperation, and, as important as anything else, raising money.

The Rusk family moved from their rented house in Washington to Scarsdale, New York, and Howard became a Manhattan commuter. "I got on the train a little before eight A.M. and I was very fortunate in those early days because a couple of friends invited me to fill in one of the train bridge games. This was a highlight of my day. I played bridge going in every morning and I hated to get into the station. The game really saved my life. I'm sure I should have been reading *The Times,* or whatnot, but I enjoyed playing so much, and it sort of took me out of things."

By this time Howard Rusk was totally committed, both emotionally and professionally, to a crusade that would consume virtually all of his time for the rest of his life. He was the preacher, and rehabilitation the gospel.

"Glad and the kids suffered in those days because I had to leave early and get home after they were in bed. We did spend weekends together. We had lots of friends, but didn't party much because I had to go out and speak so many evenings," Rusk said.

That first year in New York, when Rusk made "a very meager living writing the column for *The Times* and organizing the first program at Bellevue, going through all the administrative red tape," he spoke to more than four hundred groups.

"I'd speak at breakfasts, lunches, cocktail parties, rubber-chicken dinners at the Waldorf, wherever I could get a group of people to sit still long enough to listen." Once Rusk practically blacked out on his feet before a large group but found out later he had kept right on talking.

Rusk told his audiences:

"Eyes and ears and legs and arms don't make a man. Spirit makes a man. In our society today we don't pay for strength, we pay only for what you have in your head and your hand.

"There can be an advantage to disadvantage. People have a tremendous ability to overcompensate for disability. We have also learned that it isn't enough just to meet the physical needs of people, you need also to meet the emotional, social, vocational, and educational needs. Said a simpler way, it would be a little foolish for us to spend ninety days to teach a paraplegic to walk—which is our average training time— if he had such an anxiety that he wouldn't go outside the house. And if you meet that need, and then you send him home to a third-floor walkup where he's going to be a prisoner for the rest of his life, you've done him no great service.

"If you meet these needs, and don't take the last step, help him get the kind of job he can do within the limits of his disability, but to the hilt of his ability, then you haven't fulfilled your obligation to the severely disabled patient."

Rusk knows there is an advantage to disadvantage. He has seen it in thousands of patients over the years. He feels the obligations to the handicapped people he talks about and he lives to help fulfill them. He successfully enlisted the personal help of Presidents Roosevelt, Truman, and Eisenhower, not to mention the corporate presidents he lobbied for funds and encouraged to hire thousands of handicapped workers. He has convinced business and industry to produce entire lines of stoves, cabinets, clothing, and other devices made in a way, that the handicapped can manipulate them more easily. The electric typewriter, for example, was developed by IBM as the answer to the needs of a quadriplegic patient who wanted to write but had only feeble movement of one finger.

"Put our paraplegics at a bench job that requires upper-arm strength and hand skill, and they will kill the ordinary worker productionwise, because they're working with the overdeveloped muscles with which they walk, their shoulder and arm muscles. We have shown time and again that properly trained and placed, the disabled have a better production rate, lower accident rate, lower absentee rate, and nine times less labor turnover than the normal working side by side with them," Rusk boasts to anyone who will listen.

In 1954 he presented the statistics on eight thousand disabled persons who had been removed from the public assistance rolls after rehabilitation. He revealed that the individuals in this group earned more than $14 million in their first working year and paid more than a million dollars in federal taxes.

But that was many years later. Back at the end of his first year in New York, as Rusk made his speaking rounds looking for friends and funds for rehabilitation, his Midwestern "pioneer tradition of self-reliance" began to catch up with him.

"I was going home on the train one night after working a sixteen-hour day. I had spoken at meetings and all kinds of things, was dead tired. And I had started feeling guilty and embarrassed every time I asked someone for help. I had never asked for help in my life, really, before I got into rehabilitation, except for a couple of little research projects I did in St. Louis.

"I really felt uncomfortable and I said to myself, 'If you're going to continue to feel this way, you'd better get the hell out of this program and get back to the regular practice of medicine.' So I asked myself if I was getting anything out of it for myself. The answer was no. I asked if I was doing it because I thought it would help people. The answer was yes. 'If that is honestly and absolutely the way you feel,' I thought, 'you'd better get off the dime and get rid of this.' I made up my mind that night and never had any hesitation after that."

Rusk adjusted to his new way of life. But that is not to say that his medical colleagues understood what he hoped to accomplish. In those days it was difficult for a doctor to imagine how rehabilitation could be exciting or challenging. It was the drudgery of medicine, "an absolute stepchild." Doctors were just too busy for rehabilitation. They were too interested in high fevers and bizarre medical problems. They wanted to diagnose a rare disease, perform a delicate operation. Few saw, as Rusk did, that "No All-American's eighty-yard run can compare with a quadriplegic's heroic efforts to push a button through a buttonhole."

Instead many physicians saw Rusk's rehabilitation dreams as a giant social service boondoggle. For years after the war many of his St. Louis colleagues referred to his activities as "Rusk's Folly."

"Those criticisms hurt," he admits. "But you consider the source and often you don't pay much attention. But sometimes they hurt very much. Realize that if you sit on the top step you're the first person to get shot at, and if you get your head up a little there's always a tremendous amount of jealousy."

In June of 1946 the American Medical Association was meeting in Atlantic City, and while there Rusk met with surgeon Frank Lahey, head of the famous Lahey Clinic.

"Frank was a very direct person and a very acid guy. He said, 'Howard, when are you going to give up on this boondoggle, or whatever it is you're doing, and get back to the practice of medicine?' "

Lahey turned to Mrs. Rusk and said: "You know, your husband was a very good internist."

"I'm not going back, Frank," countered Rusk. "There are a lot of very good internists. But I have a deep feeling about this and nobody else is willing to stick out their neck and try to do something about it. I believe there are things we can do to help severely disabled people that we aren't doing. I'm going to try with all that I have to do something about it."

"All I think is that you're a little crazy," Lahey said.

But in a letter to Rusk two years later he had changed his tune.

Dear Howard,
I just returned from a meeting of the Western Surgical Society out in Utah and I saw one of my classmates, a bril-

liant distinguished surgeon who has suffered a stroke. He's
paralyzed on one side of his body and he can't speak a word.
I've been asking around, trying to figure out what can be done
for him, and I keep hearing from other doctors that you've
got the only place where he might be helped. Will you please
take him in? He's a wonderful man and he badly needs help.
I'll deeply appreciate anything you can do.
    Sincerely,
    FRANK
P.S. I think I gave you bad advice two years ago.

Lahey's friend was accepted, of course, and helped quite
a bit at Rusk's institute. Lahey's change in attitude reflected
the beginning of changes in attitudes toward rehabilitation
across the board. One of the best ways of gaining converts,
especially among skeptical doctors, was to accept their friends
and relatives for treatment.

Rusk's Folly was progressing very well indeed. From the
original concept, when rehabilitation programs were limited
to those with specific orthopedic needs, the categories were
eventually expanded. Cardiac and pulmonary cripples, the
mentally ill and cancer victims all required therapy as "whole"
people. Rusk imagined an institute that would bring together
"all of the rehabilitation resources of the community with those
of industry and labor in the existing social and governmental
agencies." Institutions for incurables were the farthest thing
from his mind. He visualized a program under one roof that
would offer help to people in need of "physical rehabilitation,
psychosocial treatment and adjustment, vocational guidance
testing and retraining," as he wrote in a 1946 *New York Times*
article called "Forgotten Casualty: The Disabled Civilian."

Naturally it was Rusk's exposure to these forgotten casualties, broken spiritually and physically, that helped him formu-
late his theories. Rusk learned that these people would work
toward their own rehabilitation every bit as hard as he would.

Few of them were actually Rusk's patients, for in his capacity as professor and director of the NYU Institute of Rehabilitation Medicine, Rusk has seen only a handful of patients over the years on a fee-for-service basis. But almost all of the hundreds of patients at the institute consider themselves to be Howard Rusk's patients. When he takes visitors on personally guided tours, they are often surprised at how many patients Rusk knows and how many seem to know him.

The faces of thousands of patients over the years play on Rusk's memory constantly. Some have faded into a pleasant blur. But he never tires of recalling the stories of favorites.

There is the letter he received in the early days of the Rehabilitation Service at Bellevue Hospital. It was from a young Tennessee girl who had read about Dr. Rusk's program in a Memphis newspaper.

> Dear Dr. Rusk:
>
> I am a 23-year-old paraplegic. I do believe that if I could get the right treatment and care, I could walk again, somehow, some way.
>
> Since I was in a hospital in 1941, nothing has been done for me. I was only left with that eternal word, "Time." Now I have learned to my stark horror that the longer I go without walking, the less likely it will be that I shall ever walk again.
>
> I am aware of the fact that paralyzed patients do not recover by sheer magic, and that it is a long, hard struggle at best. I am aware of how presumptuous it is to write to you like this, but Doctor Rusk, when it comes to walking or not walking, pride and reserve fly out of the window. Is there not some possible way I could come to Bellevue Hospital? If I could drag about any old way on crutches, I could work to pay back everything I owe. My parents know nothing about my writing to you, or how frantic and depressed I have become. I'm that "little crippled girl who is so cheerful even though she is handicapped." That is because I can smile while everything inside of me is freezing and dying.

I am sure you receive thousands of letters similar to mine, so I don't expect you to read this. I suppose that is the reason I could write it so frankly.

Yours truly,
JAMIE COFFMAN

Rusk did manage to read Jamie's letter, and he knew he would try to help this girl. Since New York City law stipulated that Bellevue Hospital was an institution for city residents, anything Rusk did would be illegal. "But some things are more important than rules," he likes to say. He wrote to Jamie telling her that if she could manage to get herself to New York, he would find a way to get her admitted to his service.

When Jamie arrived she received a fictitious New York City address and Rusk signed her admission papers. The girl's paraplegia was the result of an auto accident several years before when a date was bringing the pretty teen-ager home from a dance. Jamie's father was a country doctor in a small Tennessee town, and Jamie was brought to Memphis, where the best doctors did what they could for her. Unfortunately it wasn't much. They sent her home to spend the rest of her life in bed, where she had been for the last four years.

"Only seven months after she came into our hospital she was walking on her crutches and braces like a dancer. Jamie was one of the greatest crutch walkers I have ever seen," Rusk said, like a proud father retelling the story of his baby's first steps.

Not long after Jamie was discharged from Bellevue, Rusk was invited to Paris to read a medical paper at a meeting on the subject of rehabilitation of paraplegics. Rusk thought of the pretty Southern belle and how Frenchmen would react to her. And, at his own admission, decided to resort to "a shameless bit of show business." He brought Jamie to Paris.

All the while Rusk read his paper, discussing all of the

things that could be done for paraplegics, Jamie lay on a stretcher on the stage, putting on her braces. As Rusk finished, Jamie got up on her crutches and raced back and forth across the stage.

"After that," says Rusk, " 'Mademoiselle Jamie' was the toast of Paris. All the French newspapers printed her story, and people would stop to congratulate her as she walked along the Champs Elysées."

Jamie stayed on at NYU as an instructor of paraplegics and other handicapped people. When her students falter in their efforts Jamie urges, "Come on, honey. Try again. You'll surely make it this time." The students have only to look at their teacher to know that she knows what she is talking about.

Another Rusk favorite was the Florida boy who was attending a small Connecticut college on a football scholarship. On the first play of the season he broke his neck.

"He was in a Connecticut hospital for about four or five months, being looked after by one of the doctors who had trained with us," Rusk recalled. "The boy became an avaricious student. He decided he wanted to go back to Florida to Rollins College, but they turned him down. They said they couldn't possibly take him because their campus was made up of scattered buildings, three stories high, with no elevators.

"I said I was sure he could operate and I would give him the formula if the college would give him the chance. I knew the president there, and he said they would take a chance if I would take the responsibility."

When it came near time to leave for college the boy became nervous and asked Rusk how he would get to classes without elevators.

"Well," said Rusk, "the first day you roll your wheelchair up to the bottom of the steps of the building where you have to go upstairs, and just sit there. You'll find that at class time the kids will be coming in and they'll turn to you and say, 'What are you doing down here?' And you just say, 'Well, I want to be up on the second floor, but I can't get there.'

" 'Aw,' they'll say, 'the hell with that.' Four of them will pick you up and in thirty seconds you'll be on the second floor.

"It happened that way his first day at the school and he never had any problems for four years in college. He made Phi Beta Kappa his junior year."

Rusk established a temporary center for in-patient rehabilitation in 1948 on East Thirty-eighth Street in Manhattan. There were only forty beds (later a few more were crowded in), and the Institute was in an old five-story building ill-suited for the purpose but made to do by considerable remodeling. Rusk continued his fund-raising campaigns and successfully raised several million dollars from the general public and philanthropists such as Bernard Baruch, Louis Horowitz, and the Bernard Gimbel family. This money went toward the permanent Institute of Physical Medicine and Rehabilitation, which Rusk directed. (In 1966 the name was changed to the Institute of Rehabilitation Medicine.)

The permanent Institute, at Thirty-fourth Street and First Avenue, was opened on January 25, 1951. Before the dedication ceremony there was a parade—a parade of wheelchairs and crutch walkers along First Avenue from the Institute's temporary quarters at Thirty-eighth Street. By late morning the patients had arrived at their new home and by the end of the day all had been assigned to rooms and resumed their therapy routines.

One day in 1955 Rusk and his associates at the Institute met a nine-year-old boy who once again reaffirmed their faith in the concept of rehabilitation. He even stretched the limits of their imagination concerning those who could be helped. His name was Juan Yepez, and he was from La Paz,

Bolivia. Juan was born without arms or legs. He had two little four-fingered hands that came out of each shoulder joint. Two strong, normal feet came out of each of his hip joints.

Old movies of Juan playing as a child show him rolling like a little ball to get from one place to another. He rolled like an acrobat, somersault after somersault. Or he could roll sideways, almost as fast as a normal person could walk.

"I think I first realized that I was different when I was six years old," Juan says. "That something was wrong. These children could go along and walk on shoes and move around and they wouldn't get dirty. When I rolled I got dirty and choked on dirt and I rolled over rocks and things. Sometimes I would think, 'Wouldn't it be great to roam among people and not be noticed?' To walk alongside them, watch them, and not really be different."

Dr. Terry E. Lilly, a young plastic surgeon, had been on a teaching mission in Bolivia. While there he had seen little Juan in the local mission hospital. Juan wasn't a patient, he lived there. The boy's father had left the family right after he was born. He couldn't face his son's disability. But his mother was a hard-working woman who took cleaning and housekeeping jobs in La Paz. She had a small house with a fenced-in backyard, and when she went out she left Juan in the backyard with some food and water within his reach. That's where he stayed all day, playing games that he made up. At night his mother came home to wash, feed, and love her son. When Juan was still a child his mother died of cancer, and the boy was sort of adopted by the director of the American Hospital in La Paz.

Dr. Lilly had been tremendously impressed at how bright Juan was, and he wrote to Rusk asking if there was a way the boy could be brought to the United States for rehabilitation help.

"I told Dr. Lilly that I didn't see how we could bring Juan

over. We didn't have any funds. But even in those early days I was an old enough hand at this game not to say no too quickly, so I asked them to send pictures of him and a brief medical history.

"Well, I think the Lord works in strange ways sometimes, and it so happened that the day the letter arrived Miss Mary Boyle, who had been Bernard Baruch's secretary since she was sixteen years old, was in my office. I was late for the appointment and the pictures of Juan were at the top of my mail pile. As Mary sat next to my desk she couldn't help but see them.

"She said, 'Well, what about this boy?' I told her Juan's story, but added that I didn't see how we could bring him over since we didn't have any money. She wanted to know how long he would have to be here. I said about six months."

Mary Boyle decided to pick up the tab for Juan's expenses while he was in New York. Rusk got in touch with the Bolivian airline, and they agreed to fly Juan to New York without charge. When he arrived about two weeks later his only English words were *please* and *thank you*.

"They told me I was going to the United States," he recalled. "I was real glad and happy to go because I thought it was to the next little town or down the block or something. All I knew was the area I lived in. So I saw this big plane, and suitcases, and people taking pictures. I didn't understand what was happening."

Within a month Juan had more than 150 English words in his vocabulary. He quickly became so proficient in his new language that when four Venezuelan paraplegics arrived at the Institute one Saturday morning, when there was nobody to speak Spanish, Juan was the interpreter.

Soon the boy without arms and legs was descended upon by engineers, limbmakers, doctors, and other medical support personnel who make up the total rehabilitation picture.

"We managed to have artificial legs made for him," said

Rusk. "He sat in a little bucket arrangement and his two feet went out on each side. And then we had some trousers made that were very full so you really couldn't see his feet except for a little bulge below the waist."

Dr. Allen Russek, chief of prosthetic services at the time, remembers the day that Juan tried the first prosthesis designed for him. "We were concerned primarily with the mechanics of this thing, hoping he wouldn't fall and wondering whether the hip locks would hold. And suddenly Juan looked up, and the expression on his face I'll never forget. He shouted, 'I'm walking.'"

During this time specialists also tried to fit Juan with artificial arms and hands with hooks, but his little four-fingered hands were much more sensitive than the artificial arms. Juan quickly learned that by getting in a certain position he could write and feed himself and dress and generally meet all his daily living needs.

Juan continued to progress and he went to a neighborhood parochial school where he did very well in his studies. In the meantime he had become king of the children's ward. He helped with the other youngsters and even learned to defend himself by wrestling so he could hold his own if others made fun of him.

On Christmas and Easter young Juan came home with Dr. Rusk to spend the holidays with his family. He especially enjoyed the company of Rusk's grandchildren, and they became great friends. "Juan was the best Easter egg hunter I've ever seen, because he could roll under the sofas and the chairs and find more Easter eggs than any other kid in his age group," Rusk said.

From time to time, as Rusk lectured to different medical groups who visited the Institute, he brought Juan in to demonstrate how much could be done for a severely disabled person. "Juan loved it, because he felt that he was helping someone else. I remember one day he came in and dem-

onstrated for ten or twelve people, and he was a sensation, captivated the whole group. They were deeply impressed, and after the meeting we went up on the elevator together, and I said to him, 'You know, Juan, you were really wonderful today. You're my partner.' And he looked up at me and said, 'Don't say that. I am not your partner. I am your son.' "

As Juan grew older he began to encounter the problems that involve all young adolescents. Particularly he was bothered by a sexual-identity crisis. It was especially severe in Juan, who wondered whether he could be normal sexually and if his physical defect was hereditary, one he could pass to offspring.

One of his doctors recalled that "Juan was worried that because of his multiple handicaps he would also be inadequate from a sexual standpoint and after examining him carefully it was possible to assure him that whatever his disability meant to him there were no sexual organs involved. He had all of the functional capacity and potential of any nondisabled individual."

When Juan finished high school he wanted to go to college. A suitable Spanish-oriented school was found in California, and Juan departed. But he didn't like the school much and kept talking about going back home to Bolivia.

Juan was brought back to New York and sent through a vocational counseling service at one of the universities. He showed a very high aptitude in mathematics. "We should have had some inkling of this because since he was a little boy he had been the best chess player at the Institute. He could beat the normal people and he got great joy out of it," Rusk said.

Juan was trained as a computer programmer through IBM's regular course. A job was arranged for him in Bolivia with Comibol, the nationalized tin service.

The time drew near for Juan to return to Bolivia, and all of his friends helped prepare his sendoff. A local department store arranged for tailors to outfit him with special clothes. And since he was now twenty-one, a grown man, the Institute's physicians arranged for him to grow a few inches—by extending his artificial legs.

"We had a going-away party and flew him by helicopter out to the airport. I'll never forget his face. He was so wistful, and frightened, and determined, loving and scared all in one," Rusk recalled.

Unfortunately when Juan got back to Bolivia the man in charge of the job he was supposed to get refused to give it to him because of his disability. Even though Juan could get back and forth to work, in and out of his chair, and perform very well, he was refused the job.

The boy was desolate. But word began to get around that this determined young man had a job that was being denied him because of his disability. The radio and newspapers took up Juan's story, and the pressure on the prospective employer mounted to the point where he had to give the boy a job. It wasn't the job that had been promised—the salary was only about half—but it was a job. Unfortunately Juan now began to have other problems, with people overcharging him for food and shelter and generally taking advantage of his disabilities.

"The worst problem he had," said Rusk, "was that his own people couldn't accept him. What had happened to Juan in the United States was hundreds, maybe thousands of years ahead of what they had known basically as primitive Indian people.

"I had promised him when he left that if he couldn't make it he could come back. But he didn't want to do that because it would have meant failure, so he stuck it out."

In 1971 Juan met a young widow and the two fell in love. They were married, after living together for a while. They had a child—a perfectly normal baby girl they named Patricia. Glad and Howard Rusk were named the child's godparents.

"You can imagine the anguish that I went through while this child was coming," Juan wrote to Rusk. "I had seen all the pictures about birth defects at the Institute. But she is normal and we're so happy."

Acting more like a doting parent than a consulting physician, Rusk admits, "It's sort of a fairy tale. Juan will never come back now. I don't think he could or would want to. But under great odds I know of no other patient who has conquered such severe disabilities, first physical disabilities, then his family problems. He learned a new language, new ways of life, new ways to walk, an all-new relationship with people. Then he went back to his own country and went through all of it again."

It is an interesting sidelight that the artificial limbs designed for Juan became prototypes for the artificial limbs developed years later for children who suffered multiple birth deformities after their mothers used the drug thalidomide.

He collects dolls, this cigar-smoking, six-foot evangelist for the world's disabled millions. Each of his scores of dolls is from a different nation, a nation to which Howard Rusk has a link. Perhaps it has been a patient, or an intern, or a physician who has learned from him. Or perhaps Rusk has helped set up a rehabilitation program as he has done in Guatemala, Korea, Australia, Japan, Finland, Turkey, Brazil, and dozens of other lands.

His biggest contribution is that he was a doctor, a doctor who could look at people in another way. "Just because you can't carry ten loads of hod up a ladder doesn't mean there's something wrong with you. It just means you can't carry hod."

The world's attitude toward the disabled has come a long way since the early 1920s, when a pre-med student helped raise money to buy a wooden leg for his fraternity's crippled houseboy.

Half a century later there remains plenty to be done for

the world's severely disabled, and nobody knows it better than Howard Rusk. Although well past age seventy, he still puts in full days at the Institute of Rehabilitation Medicine, which will someday no doubt be renamed The Rusk Institute. Occasionally he'll talk wistfully of retiring soon and becoming an emeritus professor. But he quickly goes back to the pile of correspondence waiting on his desk, or answers his phone, or consents to yet another interview, or accepts just one more date to speak to a luncheon group or at another rubber-chicken dinner at the Waldorf.

And when a group of visiting physicians who want to bring some of the latest rehabilitation concepts back to their own nation ask to call on him, they are welcomed. Rusk the humanitarian, the educator, the physician, the salesman, shows them around the Institute as if he personally sweated out that first tortuous step with every single paraplegic patient.

In a way, he has, this one-time doctor to society folk. And that's why they call him Dr. Live Again.

4 C. WALTON LILLEHEI:
Master plumber of the heart

In the summer of 1951 Dorothy Eustice lay dying of advanced heart disease in the University of Minnesota Hospital.

C. Walton Lillehei, a young instructor in surgery, dropped by to visit the red-haired teen-ager one day. It wasn't really a professional visit. Lillehei's family knew Dorothy's family, and since he had recently been sick himself he knew how bad it was to be cooped up in a hospital bed day after day. He chatted with Dorothy for a while and looked over medical records.

There was little in them to cheer the doctor. The girl's condition was extremely poor. The X rays in her chart showed that her heart was huge, a sign that the defect borne within it was causing massive overwork by the muscular pump.

A few weeks later Dorothy Eustice died. Lillehei went to her autopsy and discovered that her killer was merely a hole—the size of a half-dollar and in the wall between the two upper chambers of her heart. The unnatural shunt had drastically cut the pump's efficiency and caused it to overwork fiercely. When a muscle works hard it grows, and Dorothy's heart muscle had grown to the point of being grotesque. In the process other parts of the heart had also been damaged. But it was that hole that killed her.

"When I looked at that dead girl's heart it was really a stimulus to me," Lillehei recalled later. "You could have sewed that hole up, you know, in three or four minutes if you could just get at it. But you couldn't get at it inside the heart, so Dorothy was dead."

Fifteen years after the girl's death Lillehei explained that a person such as himself is "driven to progress by some catastrophe . . . some failure, some need that you can't fill. Then you say, 'We've got to do something about this.' In other words, you are forced to think about things."

Medicine, particularly surgery, was far from primitive in 1951. Lifesaving techniques such as blood transfusions and drugs such as penicillin were already available. Safe surgical anesthesia had been perfected and was an important factor in allowing the most radical operations to be performed with increasing confidence. The scalpels of the world's skilled surgeons had already penetrated the innermost portions of the human body. The stomach, the lungs, even the brain had been successfully probed surgically.

Yet even in 1951 patients who had tiny defects within their hearts died, for surgeons still had no way of getting inside that muscle's walls to mend a small hole, sew in a patch, or cut away bits of damaged tissue that interfered with normal function. The fist-sized miracle pump, whose beat has always been synonymous with life itself, was an almost complete barrier to surgery.

A few bold surgeons had already performed some surgical repairs outside of the heart by 1951. Beginning in 1938 Dr. Robert Gross in Boston led the way with a pioneering operation that shut down a fetal blood vessel known as the patent ductus—it is a conduit necessary to a fetus's life before birth but must close soon after. In the normal infant this occurs automatically. Gross learned to provide help when nature failed.

In 1944 in Baltimore Alfred Blalock with Helen Taussig performed the first blue-baby operation. This surgery didn't cure the congenital heart defects known as tetralogy of Fallot, but ameliorated them and drastically improved the condition of the children who suffered. And in the late 1940s Dwight Harken in Boston and Charles P. Bailey in Philadelphia pioneered a method of slipping a finger, with a tiny surgical knife attached to its tip, into a beating human heart to separate the leaflets of a mitral valve that had been partially sealed by scarring, usually from rheumatic fever. This operation was literally a "stab in the dark," and it essentially summarized the state of heart surgery at the time. It's not that these operations didn't help—at the time they were viewed as little short of miraculous. But as so often happens the pioneers seem primitive when revisited years later.

In 1951 there was not yet a method of operating on an open, bloodless heart, where a surgeon could actually see what he was doing to the inside of the organ the ancient Greeks referred to as "the Acropolis of the body." Perhaps it was partially due to the many superstitions surrounding this Acropolis that there were actually only a few physicians even trying to solve such problems at the time.

At the University of Minnesota, a major center for innovative medicine and surgery, there was already a tradition of studying how to correct the problems of the defective heart. And those problems were consuming most of the time of two promising beginners, Walt Lillehei and his close friend John Lewis.

"We were young," the former recalls, "and had finished our surgical training and were staying on staff as instructors or assistant professors. We had a good deal of time, too, because on a big university hospital staff there are many experienced people around and obviously if somebody has cancer of the colon or cancer of the stomach or ulcers, the senior surgeons would be the ones called in to do most of the surgery. So our attention turned to the laboratory, and in particular, the problems of operating in the heart."

Not only did these Minnesota medicine men turn their attention to the human heart, notes British medical historian Dr. Robert Richardson, but everything the "fantastic team of Walton Lillehei and his associates . . . touched seemed to turn to gold."

Clarence Walton Lillehei entered the University of Minnesota at age fifteen. But even before that, recalled his father, a Minneapolis dentist, Walt amazed both friends and family with his unusual manual dexterity—he could break down and reassemble his bicycle or his father's Ford with ease.

Walt (he never used Clarence) was the oldest of three sons, all of whom attended high school, college, and medical school in Minneapolis.

Walt's high grades enabled him to knock a year off his premed studies and he entered the University of Minnesota Medical School at age seventeen. He finished his internship in 1942 and was swept into the army medical corps as a first lieutenant. At first the young physician was attached to a combat group in Europe, and later he ran a field hospital at Anzio. When he was discharged in early 1946, Lillehei had earned a Bronze Star and the rank of lieutenant colonel.

As a medical student, as well as on the battlefield, Lillehei had become interested in surgery. He had been particularly impressed by the lectures and reputation of Owen Wangensteen, the University's famous chief of surgery. Just before his army discharge Lillehei had applied to Wangensteen's department for a position as a resident in surgery. But a form letter turned him down.

Such adversity just raised his desires. Fortunately Walt knew something about the way the Minnesota Medical School worked. He was well aware that refusals such as he had received meant little unless they came from Wangensteen himself

—and before he would give up on his goal that's just what he would have to hear. One Thursday afternoon Lillehei visited Wangensteen, who was world renowned as a great innovator and teacher of original surgical procedures. Wangensteen was also particularly fond of home-grown medical talent—he, too, was born, raised, and educated in Minnesota —and that may be one reason that after a very short conversation with Walt Lillehei he said to himself, "There's always money for the right man."

He told Lillehei: "Well, go on downstairs and get a white coat and go to work. Tell the administration people I said to fix it up."

Lillehei did just that, and in his next four years of surgical residency and graduate study in physiology he established a reputation as a researcher and surgeon of great promise.

The promise was almost broken one winter morning in 1950 as the young surgeon stood shaving in the bathroom of his home. He massaged the foam into the stubble on his face and neck, but when his fingertips reached the joint of his left jaw they stopped. His surgeon's eyes glanced into the foggy mirror, and his surgeon's fingers automatically began to probe. No question about what they found. It was a lump.

"Goddamnit," he muttered. "I have a tumor."

It was a tumor of his parotid gland, probably benign, but a nuisance nevertheless. First of all, he thought, it would probably spoil his day. He had been up early because as Wangensteen's senior resident he had many more things to do than there were hours in a day—surgical rounds, patient visits, then back to the laboratory where he was doing fascinating research on chronic heart disease in dogs. Only the night before Walt had worked late in the physiology laboratory. And true to the standing joke among his students, at midnight when one of them made the usual rounds to feed the lab animals he also brought a hamburger for Dr. Walt.

And now this tumor. He wondered when he would even have time to schedule an operation for its removal. Actually such tumors of the parotid gland are rarely malignant and Lillehei was frankly more put out than he was worried. He did know, however, that surgery on the parotid gland could be tricky, for the seventh nerve—the motor nerve for the entire face and eye—runs right through the gland, between its deep and superficial lobes. Damage to that nerve could result in total or partial facial paralysis.

Fortunately there was a doctor on the hospital staff who was especially skilled in this kind of surgery, and Lillehei asked him to perform the operation—"How about on a holiday?" The small tumor was successfully removed on Lincoln's Birthday.

According to hospital routine the tissue specimen was taken to the laboratory where technicians embedded it in wax, sliced it, stained it, and studied the cells under high-powered microscopes. This procedure would confirm diagnosis and screen the tissue for malignancies not yet visible to the naked eye. When the pathologists were finished scrutinizing the tissue from Lillehei's gland they wrote a single word in the pathology logbook: "Negative."

But they lied. That specimen was not negative. They all agreed that it looked as if it was malignant. Somebody went to the chief and gave him the report. The "negative" had been entered into the laboratory book in case Lillehei himself decided to check it (which he did). After all, no sense in unnecessarily disrupting the routine of a brilliant young scientist-physician. For, as Wangensteen noted to a few colleagues, even the best pathology laboratories can make a mistake, particularly with such a rare cancer as this one.

So the chief ordered hair-thin slices of Lillehei's tumor sent to three of the nation's top pathology experts.

From each laboratory came the same report: lymphosarcoma.

Wangensteen's bright young man had cancer; there was no question about it.

The operating-room phone rang one morning in April,

while Chief Resident Lillehei was in the middle of a chest operation. He was removing bits of gland from the chest of a woman who was undergoing a superradical mastectomy.

A nurse answered the phone and conveyed a message: "Dr. Lillehei, Dr. Wangensteen wants to see you right away."

"Tell him I'm in the middle of an open thoracotomy and the chest is open. I'll come as soon as I'm finished."

The nurse passed his word.

"No, Doctor. He wants you right now."

"For God's sake," Lillehei griped, "what's so important?" But he called in another chest surgeon to finish the operation and went to Wangensteen's office.

"Walt, I'm afraid that tumor of yours was a lymphosarcoma," Wangensteen said, and he reported what had transpired since the surgery.

"Do you remember last month in Denver when I asked you to room with me at that convention?" Wangensteen asked. "I did that so I could get a picture of your health. You sure seemed healthy."

Indeed, Lillehei's reputation as an iron man on the job was equaled by his reputation as a carefree party-goer.

Wangensteen now was clearly worried, however, and faithfully explained the various treatment alternatives to his student, who already knew his options perfectly well.

"The conventional form of treatment is obviously X-rays. But I personally think you should have a wide surgical excision, because we have had such good results with lymphosarcoma."

Wangensteen knew what he was talking about; he was an expert's expert in this kind of radical cancer surgery.

Lillehei said he would have to consider the matter for a few days and brought the grim report home to his wife, a former nurse he had married when he was an intern at Minneapolis General. He ought to go through with the surgery, they decided.

On May 1, 1950, Lillehei underwent a twelve-hour operation performed by the three best surgical teams Minnesota could muster—and they were a match for any in the world. The first team removed the complete parotid gland and a bit of the surrounding tissue. The second team did a radical neck dissection, removing all the tissues that might harbor tiny, suspect lymph glands. Then Wangensteen moved in with his team, split the patient's breastbone and removed all of the lymph glands to which a lone cancer cell might have spread and established a virulent new colony.

In the weeks following the successful surgery came the series of postoperative X-ray therapy that Lillehei had prescribed for himself as a double precaution against any secondary cancers.

"I was kind of knocked out for a while," he recalls. "It was August or September before I got back to work." In fact, it wasn't until well after the new year that Lillehei began to feel like himself once again.

The radical operation in which much of the tendons and muscle tissue of one side of his neck had been removed left Lillehei with a striking, lifelong physical deformity. South African Dr. Christiaan Barnard, one of Lillehei's students and the world's first heart transplanter, described it as "a declivity in his neck; one expected at first that his head would topple over to the side. It did not, of course, being sustained by auxiliary muscles and, even more, by an interior strength of mind and spirit that only later I would come to know and respect."

During the same meeting of the American Surgical Association at which Wangensteen roomed with Lillehei to observe his health, W. G. Bigelow, a Canadian surgeon, reported on his experimental open heart surgery in dogs.

To slow the flow of blood through the heart safely and effectively, Bigelow and his associates had lowered the animal's body temperature, a procedure called hypothermia. Bigelow hadn't invented this method. It had been used by many over the years. But in the Canadian's studies on dogs he found that he could reduce "the oxygen requirements of the body sufficiently to allow exclusion of the heart from the circulation, thereby permitting intracardiac surgery under direct vision."

This work was based on a simple chemical law: If you reduce the temperature of a system by about 7 degrees Centigrade you cut the speed of any chemical reaction within that system in half—in other words it takes the reaction twice as long to occur.

It was pretty well known that the human brain could go up to about four minutes without oxygen before it began to die, so if the temperature of the human body was dropped from 37 degrees Centigrade to about 30, that time could be doubled to about eight minutes—almost enough time to get in and sew up some of those holes in the easier-to-reach parts of the heart.

When he returned to Minnesota, Lillehei's friend and colleague John Lewis began laboratory work almost immediately, and his great enthusiasm for hypothermia seemed to be warranted. Lillehei helped in the cooling work, and in return Lewis helped Lillehei in his research. Lillehei was working on another method of clearing the heart for surgery. While he believed there was considerable merit to the hypothermia technique, he thought its limitations could never be expanded to allow ideal surgical conditions. These, he reasoned, could come only from a circulation and oxygenation system that could bypass the heart altogether.

By the middle of 1952, Lewis's laboratory work on hypothermia had progressed to the stage at which he was ready to use the technique on a patient. And on September 2, 1952, not much more than a year after Dorothy Eustice died, a five-year-old girl who was sickly and underdeveloped, because she had been born with a hole between the two upper chambers of her heart, was operated on by Drs. Lewis, Richard Varco, and Lillehei.

After cooling the girl's body with ice water, the surgeons took little more than five and a half minutes to sew up the hole, not even an inch across, that would soon have killed her. When the girl's body was rewarmed, her heart took over beautifully, and the operation was an unqualified medical success—the first successful operation inside the heart performed under direct vision.

With that success, of course, the body-cooling operation grew rapidly at Minnesota, and the word quickly spread around the country and the world.

Throughout 1952 and 1953 the Minnesota team did about seventy-five more open heart operations using hypothermia to slow the flow of blood as well as the other body reactions. The mortality statistics were excellent—only about 10 percent died as a result of the operations. Enthusiasm among the surgical fraternity continued to grow, and open heart procedures under hypothermia were extended to areas beyond the upper chambers of the heart, areas where defects were likely to be not only more complicated but more difficult to get at as well. In order to obtain enough time to perform these operations, the doctors had to reduce the body temperature more and more. Now hypothermia's limitations really began to show, for this made the heart irritable and difficult to restart normally. Soon it became obvious to the elite—but growing—group of surgical heart specialists around the world that excellent work could be done inside the heart with patients in a hypothermic state, but limitations of this technique were insurmountable; and the most severe of them was a maximum of eight or ten minutes of operating time inside the heart.

The best answer to the problem of obtaining more time inside the living heart would be some kind of a machine that could take over the heart's pumping function as well as the lungs' oxygenating function. Such a device would have to be safe, relatively simple to operate, and, if it was ever to be widely used, of course, it had to be inexpensive.

The idea for a machine to temporarily replace the heart and the lungs had been pioneered in the 1930s by Dr. John H. Gibbon, Jr., at the Massachusetts General Hospital. In experimental animals he devised a method in which "the blood was short-circuited around the obstruction in the pulmonary artery and a good part or all of the work of the heart and lungs was temporarily taken over by artificial means."

When Gibbon left Boston to become professor of surgery at the Jefferson Medical College in Philadelphia, he brought his methods with him. In 1937 he reported that his was probably the first "successful temporary substitution of an entirely mechanical apparatus for the heart and lungs of an animal." He used dogs, which were particularly suited to this kind of work because of their anatomical resemblance to humans.

Gibbon had been following in the footsteps of medical men who for decades had been successfully oxygenating single organs such as the liver or kidneys during physiology studies. In the early 1950s Gibbon began to use his mechanical heart-lung device on human patients, and after a number of failures he finally performed a successful open heart operation with the artificial bypass in May, 1953. Unfortunately, however, Gibbon's apparatus and techniques were extremely complex and didn't lend themselves readily to widespread or even repeated use. Indeed, Gibbon himself repeatedly failed at attempts to duplicate his single success.

But Gibbon had no monopoly on interest in heart-lung machines. At Minnesota Dr. Clarence Dennis had spent four years developing a pump oxygenator, work that culminated in 1951 in an unsuccessful operation on a patient. Later in the same year Dennis left Minnesota to become chief of surgery at the New York Downstate College of Medicine. He took his heart-lung apparatus along with him and left behind several thousand dollars as a token payment. Wangensteen decided to put this previously unbudgeted money at Walt Lillehei's disposal for his own coronary-bypass research.

Dennis had taken his actual apparatus with him. But there were plenty of published accounts of exactly how it worked and how it was built. Similar plans were easily found for the mechanical heart-lung devices of Gibbon and others as well. But Lillehei wanted to start anew. He believed that none of the other pump oxygenators were so far advanced that some totally new approaches shouldn't be considered. Indeed, Lillehei told Wangensteen, he was sure something far simpler than the "Rube Goldbergs" already in use would be possible.

Lillehei's first goal was to find an effective pump.

This might seem like a simple enough matter but had actually been a most serious problem in earlier heart-lung machine research. The mechanical action of most pumps invariably battered and bruised the fragile blood cells and harmed their ability to function properly within the circulatory system. A pump that so damaged the blood was unacceptable. The researchers also found that two pumps were really necessary —one to take blood out of the body and another to send it back. Both had to work at exactly the same speed, for if one were too fast or too slow, the body could become fatally bloated or, at the other extreme, drained.

One of Lillehei's maxims was never to eliminate an idea, no matter how simple it sounded, until it had been tested and shown to be clearly impossible. So he was willing to consider any kind of pump that might fulfill his criteria—even another living pump, such as an animal's heart.

In one early series of experiments, Lillehei actually used a cow's heart that had been obtained from a local meat-packing plant. Although this was a "primitive" method, to say the least, the cow's heart helped Lillehei establish a valuable principle—its two sides acted as an automatically balanced double pump, one side removing exactly the same amount of blood that the other returned. It reminded Lillehei of a pump he had once seen in a Minnesota milk-processing plant, used for pumping milk. He ordered one and found that, indeed, it was particularly suited to his special needs because the milk—or in this case, the blood—never came into contact with the pump's working surfaces. The fluid was channeled through plastic tubes which were massaged by a dozen steel fingers that oscillated against the tubing in rotation and forced the fluid along the lines. Moreover, two pumps could easily be operated from the same motor, thus automatically keeping balance.

Now that Lillehei had a pump he was confident would suit his needs, he had to determine just how much work it would have to do. How long could circulation actually be stopped without damage to the heart itself?

This was a vital question, and although it may seem elementary, nobody had yet carried out a study of the problem. In fact, there was considerable disagreement in the published experiences of various researchers. Some reported that the hearts of their experimental dogs could survive only a few moments of blood stoppage, but others claimed the time limit to be an hour or more.

Working with Dr. Morley Cohen, a resident surgeon from Winnipeg, Lillehei found the reason for the discrepancy. Independently Drs. A. Andreasen and F. Watson in England had made the same discovery a few weeks earlier. What they found was that the various researchers were getting such differing results because of the methods they used to stop the flow of blood through the heart itself. The scientists whose dogs had died within minutes were completely cutting off the blood flow. Those who had greater success, however, were blocking blood flow from the veins leading to the heart in such a way that they left open a tiny, rather insignificant vein called the azygos. Blood flowing through the azygous vein thus dribbled through the heart continuously and was sufficient to keep the dogs alive for half an hour or more without apparent harm.

The Lillehei-Cohen reduced-flow principle could really simplify matters, for heart-lung machine mechanics in the past had been going on the assumption that normal blood flow needed to be maintained. Now Lillehei and Cohen had to quantify their data, nail down just how much blood flow the heart needed. But they didn't have any sophisticated fluid-measurement apparatus in the Millard Hall laboratory. In a less than brilliant but nevertheless fascinating improvisation, the doctors used a latex-rubber condom—it was sterile, flexible, and the right size—to catch the azygous flow for a few seconds, measure it, and determine just what the flow rate through the small vein was. They found that as little as one-tenth the normal blood flow through the heart was sufficient, and thus a second crucial principle was established in their work.

"At that point," Lillehei recalls, "we had hypothermia in the back of our minds, but we thought at the time it would be awfully complicated to try to combine hypothermia with the reduced-flow principle."

However, when the heart plumbers considered the fact that they needed only about a tenth of the amount of blood they had originally thought necessary, the next idea was to use the animal's own lungs to oxygenate the blood. All they had to do was install some auxiliary tubing to temporarily reroute most of the blood flow around the heart and back through the lungs, from which freshly oxygenated blood would once again flow into the body. Lillehei tried it in the laboratory on dogs, and it worked quite well; the heart was kept nicely free of blood, and it remained viable for half an hour or more.

At this point the researchers needed the self-oxygenation method since they were concentrating mainly on polishing their abilities to repair defective dog hearts. For a while they continued this system of bypassing the heart, using the animal's own lungs as oxygenators. One day, to make things easier, they decided simply to use another, healthy dog as the oxygenator. They would hook the circulatory systems of two dogs together and the "donor" dog would support the other while its heart was bypassed for surgery. The "milk pump" was used to keep the blood flow between donor and patient—and back—absolutely constant. This cross-circulation technique worked so beautifully on the dogs—almost 100 percent of the experimental animals survived—that the surgeons became increasingly intrigued with its possible use in humans.

When Lillehei tossed the idea up as a trial balloon at the University Hospital, he became the center of a raging medical controversy. Some doctors claimed that cross-circulation was foolhardy because a healthy person, as well as a patient, had to face the risks of surgery. As the debate developed, another area of conflict became apparent: pessimism. For by the time Lillehei's team had reached the point of considering cross-circulation for open heart operations on humans, perhaps a dozen operations with various mechanical heart-lung devices had been performed around the world. All but Gibbon's single successful operation had failed.

Such failures, noted Lillehei, "repeated several times in the hands of different workers, gave rise to the opinion, then prevalent, that the fault was not in the methods but rather that the problem was the 'sick' human heart. The latter, damaged by the pathology which the surgeon sought to correct by surgical means, could not be expected to tolerate a cardiotomy, especially into a ventricle, together with an extensive intracardiac procedure. It was therefore felt that this field of open intracardiac surgery was doomed to remain one of very limited application."

In 1883 a surgeon named Billroth admonished that "The surgeon who should attempt to suture a wound of the heart would lose the respect of his colleagues." Surgeons, however, had later successfully done so. Now heart surgery stood on another threshold. Prophets of pessimism again tried to block the way. They said that a sick human heart was entirely different from a healthy dog heart—on which most of the experimental open heart surgery had been performed. The doctors who were learning to repair defective hearts actually created defects in the hearts of experimental dogs and then corrected them using new surgical techniques.

And this significantly large school of pessimism continued to argue that one could never hope to take a sick, dilated, failing human heart and expect its owner to be able to stand such a radical surgical procedure.

"I didn't *know* any different," Lillehei says, "and neither did the people who were working with me. But we chose not to believe it. We continued being optimistic for some inherent reason. Our feeling was that you really could work on the sick human heart, but we really had no proof, so we wanted to go ahead with this cross-circulation."

At this point, as optimistic as Lillehei was, he still wasn't sure which bypass mechanism would best allow complicated repair work on human hearts. The cross-circulation might work, but it was a new idea. Perhaps some kind of a clever pump oxygenator would yet be developed.

Even before any of these methods had been devised, though, Lillehei knew what he wanted to do. He was optimistic about operating inside human hearts well before he was sure how— or, really, even if—he'd be able to perform the complicated repairs. He hadn't even dreamt of cross-circulation, and the pump oxygenators of those days didn't have a chance in hell. But as long ago as 1950 Lillehei was so sure open heart surgery would someday be possible that he was actually afraid he wouldn't know what to do when the opportunity arose.

To prepare himself, he began regular visits to the University of Minnesota's pathology museum, where specialists had gathered a collection of hearts with various defects. They had been removed from their former owners during autopsies and stored in formalin.

Lillehei began making his visits to the pathology laboratory because of concern over several problems. First there was the tremendous anatomical variety of the various defects. When he sought and received special permission to open some of the large glass storage jars and remove the preserved hearts to special dissecting trays, he would sit, staring at the long-dead hearts, the pungent smell of formalin burning his nostrils and causing his eyes to water, and try to visualize how he might attack a particular defect to mend it.

"I was appalled . . . very concerned. It just looked impossible. One of the reasons was obvious. These hearts had been preserved in formalin for years. But after only a month or two it no longer made any difference. They were just stiff like an old boot that's been out in the water and allowed to dry by the stove—just rigid. So it was obvious that you could learn something from these specimens, but you couldn't learn anything about how to close the defects in them."

This had Lillehei worried. He didn't have or know of a method that would allow him to operate successfully within the depths of the living human heart. But he was fretting over the chance that such a method would be developed and he wouldn't be ready to take advantage of it—"those old, tough, preserved hearts really had me worried. Those things were petrified."

He devised a special heart-study system in cooperation with the pathology residents who did autopsies for the hospital. And for the months those studies went on, Dr. Walt was probably the only surgeon in the world who was regularly roused from bed to perform "emergency" heart surgery on a corpse.

"They'd call me for every case of death from suspected congenital heart disease," Lillehei recalls. "Day or night or weekend or anytime. Any patient with the slightest suspicion that there might be a congenital heart defect had our attention.

And those cases were entirely different from the preserved specimens.

"It was far more reassuring. I think that there was actually a bit of overoptimism, because in the soft, fresh, flexible heart you could just pull the edges of the defect together and stitch it up. But sometimes the hole was too big, and we knew there was just too much tension when we pulled it together. That's when we developed the concept of using a synthetic patch for those big holes."

The long hours Lillehei and his students and associates put in at the Millard Hall laboratories helped fine-tune their prowess in the hospital's operating room. Owen Wangensteen understood this and had complete confidence that any new surgical procedures had been thoroughly tested. It was at Wangensteen's own insistence, after all, that his residents spent so much time in the laboratories learning to be scientists as well as physicians. These were major factors in his firm support of the cross-circulation project.

In March, 1954, there was a nineteen-month-old boy suffering heart failure from a ventricular defect, the kind that couldn't be successfully corrected using the body-cooling open heart surgery. Hypothermia simply didn't allow the surgeons enough time to repair the larger, more complicated defects between the two muscular pumping chambers of the heart, and the pediatricians were well aware of this. One of them, Dr. Ray Anderson, was extremely sympathetic to the possibility of having the hole in this child's heart sewn up in a cross-circulation operation. Anderson had been up to Lillehei's Millard Hall labs several times and had watched some of the dog experiments.

"Ordinarily that child would have been sent home to die," said Lillehei of the nineteen-month-old, "but we prevailed on Anderson to keep him in."

Meanwhile controversy raged within the hospital. Wangensteen finally suggested that the operation be performed when the chief of pediatrics and a couple of other doctors who didn't approve of the operation were out of town.

"That's just what we did," Lillehei recalls. "I had a little note from the chief scribbled on a piece of paper. I had asked him, finally, if it was all right to go ahead. He wrote: 'By all means, Walt, go ahead.'"

The operation went perfectly, as performed by the team of four that had worked so closely together in the laboratory— Lillehei, Richard Varco, and the two junior residents, Herbert Warden and Morley Cohen.

The nineteen-month-old boy, just days away from sure death, was attached by plastic tubes to his twenty-eight-year-old father. The father's circulatory system, heart, and lungs worked as a pump oxygenator for the son's blood while Lillehei's repairmen bypassed the diseased heart, opened it, repaired it, and sent the red fluid of life speeding through it once again. Within six months the child's mother reported her son to be as active as his normal friends.

With this initial success, the criticisms of exposing normal persons to surgical hazards to help a patient with a failing heart faded into the background.

Minneapolis saw two cross-circulation operations the next week and two a week for several months. There was a good deal of logistical planning that had to go into this lifesaving but still tricky operation, and as soon as one was finished the Lillehei team began to plan the next one. During the first year of the cross-circulation technique, Lillehei operated on forty-five patients, scoring a string of "firsts" for successfully repairing heart defects that had never been fixed before. Nineteen of those operations were successful. Now that might not sound like such a fantastic batting average, but remember that prior to the successful use of cross-circulation, all forty-five of those patients would have soon died; the "master plumbers" of the human heart had literally snatched nineteen people from the grave.

"Long before the first year was out word got around, and we had countless visitors; and this pessimism about the heart not being able to stand open heart surgery vanished almost overnight. It became obvious that the universal failure of the heart-lung machines was not a failure of the concept but a failure of carrying out the technique properly," Lillehei says.

This realization served as another strong impetus for the heart repairmen to intensify their search for other methods of bypassing the heart and getting oxygen into the blood. Cross-circulation was a good technique, but no matter how success-ful it was, it *did* put a healthy person at a small risk, and so if that small risk could be avoided, it would be preferred. So as they successfully used cross-circulation to operate, the researchers continued to look into alternative methods.

In one series of fifteen patients early in 1955 they used dog's lungs to oxygenate the blood during surgery. The animal's lung was sterilized and washed completely free of blood. Now white as a sheet of writing paper, the lung was hung in a special humidifying chamber, oxygen was forced through it and the patient's circulation was attached to it through a series of tubes and a pump. The system worked well for small pa-tients, but it, too, was fragile and complicated.

In a less complicated method that was also successful, Lille-hei and his associates used their knowledge that a very small child needed only half a dozen or so bottles of oxygenated blood in the course of an open heart operation. This small amount of blood could be taken directly from donors and held until surgery. Unfortunately the technique of arterial puncture necessary to draw oxygenated blood is relatively difficult and must be done by a highly trained person. However, Dr. Ray-mond Read, another resident, remembered reading that ve-nous blood with a high oxygen content could be obtained from a vein in the arm if the arm was first submerged for about fifteen minutes in very hot water. The heat speeds the circulation so much that blood from the arteries flows through the capillaries and into the veins while it still has most of its oxygen. This method was used successfully to supply oxygenated blood to several infants who underwent open heart surgery.

All the while, however, other residents were busy in their laboratories working on possible heart-lung machines. Almost a year to the day after the first cross-circulation operation, that technique was to be used no more. Failure was not the reason. It was success—the Minnesota team had finally developed a simple, effective heart-lung machine.

Actually there never had been a problem getting fresh oxygen into the blood of a person whose lungs were being bypassed. Cross-circulation did it, the dogs' lungs did it, and the bottled arterial blood also served the purpose well. But for years the world's medical men had been trying to devise a simple device that would put oxygen into the blood without putting either the patient or a donor in danger or putting the operating-room staff to much trouble. Mostly the researchers had given up. It was simple enough to get oxygen into the blood—some even suggested injecting pure oxygen into the bloodstream directly—but too hard to get the excess bubbles out. The problem here was that any bubble much larger than an infinitesimally small size in the blood of a patient could prove fatal.

Nevertheless, Walt Lillehei thought the idea of a bubble oxygenator had as much merit as anything else, and he was anxious to try to develop one that worked.

At about this time he was also looking for another physician to help out in the operating room during the cross-circulation surgery. In the early operations the surgeons depended heavily on the anesthesiologists to keep a close eye on the pump that maintained a balanced flow of blood between patient and donor.

For several weeks a young general practitioner named Richard DeWall had frequently visited Lillehei. He would drop by at the end of long days and tell the surgeon how much he wanted to leave his new practice and go back to medical school and concentrate on study of the heart. "He really had no special qualifications, and I was a little skeptical, but I finally decided we would take him on," Lillehei recalls. "Dick would run the pumps in the operating room and also work in the laboratory full-time on this bubble oxygenator, trying to figure a way to get the bubbles out of the blood completely."

Nobody had ever claimed that this Dr. DeWall was a genius. He had gone to medical school at Minnesota, where his grades were adequate to pass, but not at all spectacular. Still, he was persistent, sincere, and "the mechanically inventive type," so Lillehei decided to take him on as a regular resident. At Minnesota at the time, however, all of the surgical residents had to be enrolled in the graduate school as well, working on Ph.D. degrees.

DeWall filled out and submitted the various application forms for graduate school (in the meantime he had already started working for Lillehei). In due course the forms came back to Lillehei's office: The graduate school had turned DeWall down because he didn't have the required B average from medical school.

By this time DeWall had already proven himself a valuable member of the team, so Dr. Walt approached the chief for help. Wangensteen was sympathetic, but said: "I don't know, Walt. I've been around here twenty or twenty-five years and have never yet won an argument with those people in the graduate school. DeWall just can't get in here as a resident if he doesn't have a B average—guess you can't take him on."

Without joy Lillehei reported the conversation to DeWall.

"So," DeWall replied, "why not just hire me as a laboratory animal attendant?"

"If that's what you want," Lillehei said, "but that sure won't do you any good for graduate credits."

DeWall didn't care. He just wanted to work on what fascinated him—the heart and circulatory system. He was sure he could build a bubble oxygenator that would work. Within a few months he did.

It was made of plastic tubes, corks, the reliable old milk pump, and a few other small bits and pieces that could be found around any hospital's supply room. The size of this new pump oxygenator could be altered to suit the patient, and all of its parts that came into contact with blood were disposable —cost of the disposable parts: $11.

To use the device, venous blood was routed around the heart and out of the body into a tall plastic tube. Constantly bubbling through the same tube were a few dozen streams of bubbles of pure oxygen. The oxygen enters the blood here, and much of the carbon dioxide escapes through a hatch at the top of this mixing tube. Now DeWall planned two ways to get the remaining bubbles out of the blood before it was returned to the body. First he coated the inside of the upper part of the long mixing tube with a commercial antifoaming product to reduce the surface tension of the fluid thus causing the bubbles to pop. This alone was not enough, however, and an inclined return tube, where bubbles could rise while the blood flowed slowly downward, was introduced. But in order to get this inclined tube to work properly, it had to reach several feet in length. This became far too cumbersome. A bit of logical thinking helped DeWall solve the problem—he curled the debubbling tube into a spiral helix of three or four loops. Now the heavier, bubble-free blood could easily sink to the bottom, drip into a reservoir, and, fully oxygenated, be pumped back into the patient's body.

Not long after the concept was developed, the whole disposable part of the oxygenator mechanism was condensed into a couple of plastic sheets stamped together, with the oxygen tube, bubbling area, and debubbling spirals all built in. The Minneapolis doctors who developed and use it call it the "bag" or "raincoat."

Both the earlier apparatus and "the bag" had successful operating-room debuts—twenty years later essentially the same principle is still used in most heart-lung machines. Dr. DeWall, the animal attendant in Millard Hall, became very well known, of course. His name was at the top of many papers and he was invited to lecture at medical schools far and near.

And . . . oh, yes. Lillehei soon resubmitted those application forms back through the graduate school and, wouldn't you know it, Dick DeWall was accepted.

It was only years later that Lillehei learned how DeWall had actually had the last laugh—as a laboratory animal attendant he had been earning some fifty dollars a month more than he would have as a resident physician!

The new open heart surgery, with the efficient Lillehei-DeWall bubble oxygenator working as a "heart-lung machine," was only a little short of miraculous. For the first time in history thousands of patients, particularly youngsters who previously would have never lived past age ten, were able to have their innermost pumping apparatus fixed. In every major city in the world teams of heart repairmen were formed. As more doctors learned, more found new ways to help their once hopeless patients lead full and normal lives.

Success is a spoiler, however, and the heart surgeons were quickly spoiled indeed. The more success they met, the more they expected. And when they began to find that the lifesaving heart repairs they were making actually caused some of their patients to die later—well, it was frustrating to say the least.

The paradox revolved around those patients who had holes in the walls that divided the right and left ventricles of their hearts. Such defects frequently lie near portions of the heart that initiate and conduct tiny electrical impulses from the auricles to the ventricles and keep the heart's efficient beat on schedule for a lifetime.

That beat of life begins with electrical activity from a small biological pacemaker in the upper right chamber of the heart. This pacemaker, really an independent biological sparkplug with essentially no other nervous connections, spreads its impulses through the walls of both upper chambers of the heart, called atria. Immediately a specific interheart communications system transmits the impulses to the heart's pumping chambers, or ventricles. Unless disease or physical abuse damages it, our heart's pacemaker taps out its rhythm day after day in a tireless symphony of life.

When a patient has a heart defect in the wall between the right and left ventricles, the defect often lies close to the essential portions of the heart's conduction system that brings the impulses down from the auricles to the ventricles. In fact, conduction tissue was damaged in nearly one of ten early open heart operations, the damage taking place upon insertion of stitches needed to close the defect or secure an artificial patch to block it.

The result of such damage to the heart's electrical transmission fibers is often total heart block. When this occurs the heart's upper chambers may continue to contract at a normal seventy to eighty beats per minute, but the ventricles, which no longer receive clear messages from the pacemaker, plod along at a tempo of about forty beats per minute, with a propensity to slow to twenty, ten, or even zero. Since the ventricles are the pumping chambers, this seriously affects the heart's life-giving efficiency. If the heartbeat stops for more than a few seconds, the muscular ventricles may begin to fibrillate, or contract spasmodically, quivering like a lump of Jello on a plate. Ventricular fibrillation is fatal if it continues unchecked for more than a few moments, for a fibrillating heart pumps no blood.

These master plumbers had successfully entered the heart to correct its inborn defects, only to be frustrated by another complex problem. Lillehei and his colleagues began an urgent search to deal with the invariably fatal complication of complete heart block. They tried a battery of drugs that showed promise of improving the heart's rate and rhythm. They attempted to use an artificial electric pacemaker, but the bulky machine proved unwieldy and difficult to attach effectively to a child who might need it for weeks before normal heart rhythm was restored. Further, the external pacemakers at the time delivered their heart-stimulating impulses through the skin. And the voltage that was necessary—about sixty volts—made the patients twitch and jump with pain. When patients were anesthetized or otherwise restrained for this type of stimulation, quarter-sized skin ulcers developed at the point of electrode contact.

In one group of seventy of Lillehei's early open heart surgery patients, seven were victims of complete heart block. They were treated by the stimulant drugs epinephrine and ephedrine, and their hearts were jolted by outside electrical stimulation. A few of the seven survived the ordeals and managed to live a week or ten days, but not a single one of them survived to leave the hospital.

At about this time a new asthma drug, Isuprel, was introduced on the market. One of its undesirable side effects was to speed up the heart's pumping action, and this gave the clinicians the idea of using it to treat heart block. It worked, and of the first group of thirteen total heart block victims at Minnesota treated with Isuprel, seven survived to go home. Unfortunately five of them died shortly after leaving the hospital. But Isuprel could save about 40 percent of the total heart block victims. This was progress—but still not enough.

"One of the things that occurred to me," Lillehei says, "was, well, if we could stimulate the heart through the chest wall, why not put a wire right on the heart and see what happens."

With Drs. Vincent Gott and William T. Weirich, a young

resident surgeon, Lillehei set about looking into just such a method of keeping the heart going. "We recalled the classic experiment that every medical student performs in his physiology course," Lillehei said, "placing an electric wire in a turtle's heart, after removal from the body, and seeing it continue to beat for hours. We decided to carry out a similar experiment in dogs after surgically producing heart block in them. One electrode was inserted in the dog's heart and the other in the skin of the animal's chest."

Weirich, doing most of the laboratory work under Lillehei's supervision, began to solve the technical problems of attaching the fine wire directly to the heart muscle and bringing it out to the stimulator through a small incision in the skin. In dogs the wire was easily attached during surgery and just as easily removed later when it was no longer needed. The return wire needed to complete the circuit was taped onto the skin. The experimenters found that effective heart stimulation could be attained with a current of two to three volts—too small to be felt.

Of the fifty dogs tested in the laboratory, nearly all of them were maintained at normal heart rate by the artificial pacemaker. It was clear to the surgeons early in their laboratory work that this method was a lifesaver.

"After practically the first dog we could see that it was really good. I don't think there was more than an interval of a week or two before we tried it on the very next heart block patient," Lillehei recalls.

That was January 30, 1957, when Lillehei's master heart mechanics and electricians completed the first successful complete heart block treatment in humans using an electric pacemaker connected to an electrode within the heart.

The pacemaker used in the laboratory work, as well as in the early patients, was a Grass, Model S-4A Physiologic Stimulator. About half as big as a large desk, the Grass stimulator had been standard equipment around physiology laboratories for many years. It is like a console that plugs into the wall, and its various switches and dials can be set for all kinds of different strengths and frequency currents for stimulating nerves and glands in physiologic tests.

"We used the Grass for the first six or eight months," Lillehei says, "but it was a quite unsatisfactory apparatus from that standpoint. Heart block, of course, occurred in the operating room. Fortunately patients would practically never develop it after leaving there. So you had to institute treatment immediately. You couldn't wait to get the patient to the post-op unit. So we had to string a wire from the operating room to the intensive care unit and from the intensive care unit to the heart hospital which was connected to the main hospital by a ramp.

"So when we had a heart block we had our Grass stimulator —luckily it was on wheels—and we had to string those cords all over the place. Since stimulation had to be continuous, we had to move the device as far as we could until the end of its cord, and then plug it into the next socket farther up the hall and keep moving along. We were tethered to a length of cord.

"When patients started to recover they wanted to walk around. Of course they could walk around the room, but they couldn't walk any farther than the length of the wire to the machine and, of course, the machine had to be plugged into the wall. So almost immediately it was obvious that we needed a better stimulator box. The electrical system, after all, was extremely simple. All you wanted was a repetitive current. We knew that we had perfect control of the heartbeat with the device. We found on electrocardiograph that when a patient was stimulated, a heartbeat perfectly followed each stimulus."

The heart-repair team now had complete control over the heart rate of patients who suffered total heart block. Such a patient's heart rate would correspond to wherever Lillehei set the dial on their stimulator box.

By the time the Minnesota surgeons published their first

study on their initial series of artificial pacemaker patients later in 1957, they had used the method eighteen times on victims of total heart block that had occurred during the repair of holes in the heart. In quite a contrast to the complete mortality of the early heart block victims, seventeen of these first eighteen pacemaker patients lived to go home.

The single death occurred when the second electrode, taped to the patient's skin, accidentally fell off, breaking the circuit. To eliminate more such tragedies the second electrode was henceforth anchored under the skin. Later it was placed directly into the heart muscle alongside the first.

All of this success, of course, made headlines around the world—in both the medical and the lay press. However, Lillehei and his team were still not satisfied. There must be something better than depending on a machine that had to be plugged into the wall for its electric supply. A short circuit or power failure could kill a patient.

At about this time there was a young physics graduate student working in Lillehei's physiology laboratory. Robert Bruss had his undergraduate degree in electrical engineering and had observed some of the early pacemaker work.

One day Lillehei told him, "I want a little stimulator box so I can move these patients up and down the hall without being hooked to an outside source."

"Sure," said Bruss. "I can make you just what you want."

"If we can get a box like that," Lillehei replied, "we can have patients wired up for longer periods of time and we can send them home with the boxes still hooked up."

"I'll make one up," Bruss promised.

But Bruss, typical of many graduate students, became difficult to pin down, hard for Lillehei to keep in contact with. He didn't have an office and "kind of wandered around. I managed to contact him maybe once a week. As much as three or four or even five months went by, I think, and whenever I asked him about the box he always had an excuse.

He had parts on order, this or that didn't come, and so on. One day in exasperation—I didn't tell him I had given up on him, but I had—I looked around for someone else."

Fortunately for Lillehei and for future cardiac patients there was another young electrician around the medical school. Earl Baaken had been coming in on an hourly basis to repair operating-room equipment and the electrocardiograph machines which, Lillehei recalls, "were always on the fritz." Baaken and a classmate, Palmer J. Hermundslie, had a tiny electrical shop in a garage behind one of their homes. In the shop they repaired television sets to supplement their incomes. Although Baaken was a Minnesota electrical engineering graduate, Lillehei didn't know it at the time. He only knew that he needed "that box," and here was a reliable young man with a penchant for electronics.

"Earl also knew something about the heart block treatment, so I told him the same thing I told Bruss," Lillehei says. "The difference was that in less than four weeks he came back with the very first pacemaker."

It was quite a little gadget. Baaken had built the box measuring only four by two and a half by one inch thick. It held a 9.4-volt mercury battery with a 1,000-hour life. The inner parts were secured in a rubbery base to keep them from shaking loose, and the whole business was light enough for patients to carry around with ease in a small harness designed just for the purpose.

At the time Lillehei approached him, Baaken's backyard business was called Medtronics. Soon Baaken began making pacemakers for other doctors around the world, working with Lillehei and others to improve the design. Back in 1958, Medtronics had six employees, according to one of the firm's reports. "It doesn't say," Lillehei grins, "that three of them were the fellows' wives."

By 1974 Medtronics employed twenty-five hundred and produced six thousand pacemakers each month. "That figure is very interesting because nonsurgical heart block was supposedly a very rare condition. But the point was that the victims of it lived for so short a time that cardiologists were just under the impression that it was rare. It wasn't rare at all, the patients just weren't around to plague the cardiologist in his office for treatment."

Within a couple of years physicians in Buffalo, Boston, and elsewhere had devised pacemaker devices based on Lillehei's principle, but they could be implanted completely within the body, thus avoiding the danger of a wire being snagged and pulled out, as well as minimizing the chances of infection where the wires emerge through the chest wall. "I don't know why we didn't think of doing that," Lillehei says.

Walton Lillehei was a thorough researcher and a brilliant, innovative surgeon. Unlike many other surgeons who have garnered headlines, however, Lillehei was also known to his patients as a solicitous doctor who would spend a lot of time with them. He paid special attention to their needs and comforts, perhaps because of his own experience as a hospital patient.

But in addition to all of those things, Lillehei had also become a great teacher, just like Wangensteen, his own teacher. He trained many dozens of fine surgeons, among them Dr. Norman Shumway of Stanford University, the man who devised the technique for heart transplantation, and Dr. Christiaan Barnard, the man who performed the first human-to-human heart transplant.

Lillehei's special qualities as a teacher are attested to by Barnard in his autobiography, *One Life*. As Lillehei's chief resident, Barnard was beginning an operation on a seven-year-old boy who had a hole between the two pumping chambers of his heart.

"There was no trouble at the beginning. We opened the chest, exposed the heart, and prepared to loop the two veins.

The superior vena cava came into position easily. But in putting an instrument around the inferior vena cava I found a bit of tissue in front of it."

Barnard turned to the surgeon assisting him and said: "Cut that, will you!"

A scissors snipped, and blood began to spurt—Barnard had ordered the junior surgeon to cut a hole in the boy's heart.

Barnard tried to clamp the wound but succeeded only in mutilating it further. "The blood poured out now in a flood, filling the cardiac cavity. The heart continued to beat at its own irreversible pace . . ."

"Call Dr. Lillehei . . . now," Barnard ordered.

When Lillehei arrived he connected the patient to the heart-lung machine. "With the heart still not beating, but the boy held in life by the machine, Dr. Lillehei began the operation. . . . Through it all, I prayed that the child would be all right. . . ."

But when it was over, and the blood was rerouted through the boy's heart, it did not start beating again.

An hour or so after it was over, the South African managed to gather his nerves and phone Lillehei, who asked him to come up to his office.

When Barnard entered, pale and shaky, Lillehei ordered him to sit.

"Look, Chris, we've all made these mistakes that cost the lives of patients. You've made the mistake this time. The only thing you can do is to learn by your mistake. The next time you have bleeding, remember you can stop it by putting your finger in the hole. That gives you time to prepare and con-solidate yourself, to get calm, and think of what you have to do. All you had to do was put your finger in that hole. Now it's a lesson that you have learned, and I still have confidence in you, because I've made the same mistake in my life—you hear me?"

Barnard nodded.

The next day a similar operation was scheduled to take place. Barnard scrubbed and entered the operating room and began the same procedure he had performed the day before. "Dr. Lillehei stayed away until the last moment. Then he came in with his cocked head-lamp and peered into the chest," Barnard recalled.

"Good job," Lillehei said.

"Thank you," Barnard replied. At the time, he recalled, he was also thinking, "Thank you for giving me the chance to recover. Thank you for understanding how it is to lose, and how important it is to have the illusion that you can win."

That was no illusion of winning. That was the real thing, not only for Barnard, but for C. Walton Lillehei and the millions of patients who have benefited and will benefit from the techniques devised and perfected by the master plumber of the human heart.

5 IRVING COOPER:
He froze the brain

As if they were figures frozen on a frame of movie film, each person on the scene stops to listen: the X-ray technicians, the nurses, the anesthesiologist, the students, and even the surgeon who discovered the dramatic brain operation.

They are listening to two middle-aged women gossip in the corridor outside the operating theater.

"How do you feel?" one asks.

"Wonderful," comes the answer. "Just look."

Everybody looks.

What they see is a woman opening and closing her fist, spreading her fingers, and holding her arm outstretched. It is the first time in fifteen years she has been able to manage these simple movements. Lying on the stretcher that brought her out of the operating room moments before, she leans her bandage-swathed head back to relax and contemplate the normal life to which she will soon return.

An hour ago this woman, with brown eyes and brown hair (now shaved), suffered disabling and uncontrollable tremor and muscular stiffness on the left side of her body. She was just another victim of Parkinson's disease, sometimes called the shaking palsy. Now this mother of three has been relieved of the embarrassing and frightful symptoms and in two weeks, if recovery is routine, she will go home, rid of the disease that literally shakes its victims to death. Often the involuntary trembling and progressive rigidity of Parkinson's disease cuts victims off from even the simplest tasks of everyday living. They cannot walk, write, lie down, or get up. Their faces are cast in an expressionless pall, and their voices are often all but inaudible.

You have probably seen these prisoners of their own muscles. You cut a wide detour when you pass one on the street.

But now one victim's body will tremble no more. Another operation may be needed in the future, but this day in 1958 she has left the shakes behind in a Bronx hospital.

Meanwhile, on the other side of the corridor outside the operating room, the next patient waits to undergo the operation.

Now a tall man, ruggedly handsome with broad shoulders and wavy blond hair, takes the woman's tortured, trembling hand in his own. His grip is firm but gentle; his fingers are compact and powerful—nothing like the long, lithe fingers one would imagine. For this is the neurosurgeon who will perform the brain operation known around the world as the chemopallidectomy. He discovered it. He perfected it. He defended it. In the operation that part of the patient's brain called the globus pallidus will be destroyed by a few drops of absolute alcohol.

Attendants push the shaking woman's stretcher through two sets of double doors and into the operating room. In a flurry of activity she is scrubbed and the scalp area sterilized and draped. Nurses arrange shining surgical instruments on small tables as the patient lies awake, allowing her body to be situated by the masked men and women who talk to her in quiet, reassuring tones as they go about their business.

Glistening yellow-brown from the iodine scrub, her shaved head stands out on the sterile green field of surgical drapes. Bright lights in germ-free fixtures shine on the dime-sized hole the surgeon has just bored in her skull.

"Raise your left hand," the surgeon commands. The patient does, and everybody in the room watches it tremble and shake.

Now the surgeon positions himself at the woman's head, which is held firm by a viselike clamp. He begins to insert a slim, silver tube of his own design into the depths of the brain. Like a navigator among ocean reefs, the surgeon follows marked X-ray pictures of the patient's brain and gently inserts the slim tube, called a cannula, along preplotted lines toward the target area.

Local anesthetic is used only at the skull incision, for the brain itself feels no sensation. Furthermore, the patient must remain awake to assist the surgeon. The patient seems at ease, although one senses a crackle of tension in the air. Once a patient with the silver tube deep in his brain quipped, "Where's Ben Casey?"

The surgeon continues, gently, to push the tube toward the globus pallidus. Occasionally he pauses, a bell sounds, and the entire staff vacates the room. An X-ray is snapped. And as quickly as they left each of the green-clad workers returns. Several times this ritual is repeated. X-rays are developed instantly so the surgeon knows exactly how much farther he must insert the cannula. The six-inch journey through the human brain takes the surgeon and his two resident surgeons an hour or more.

When the cannula reaches the target area within the brain, the surgeon pumps air into it, inflating a tiny balloon against the globus pallidus, deep inside the brain.

The conscious patient assists the doctor by hand signals. When the surgeon begins to insert his probe, the hand rising above the operating hood is stiff and palsied. As rapidly as the guilty brain cells are squeezed into inactivity by the tiny balloon, the hand ceases to shake.

On orders from the surgeon the patient now makes a fist, spreads her fingers, touches her nose.

All is going well. If the shaking has not returned by to-

morrow the doctor will deflate the balloon and inject sixty
drops of pure alcohol through the tube to destroy the diseased
portion of the brain.

Tomorrow's activity, however, will be an anticlimax for
all those who have witnessed today's operating-room drama.
The sight of coordinated movements by a hand which only
moments earlier was crippled by tremor and rigidity is an
emotional climax.

The patient spontaneously cries out, as have many before
her, "God bless you, Dr. Cooper."

Since the mid-1950s the lame, the halt, and the spastic
have come from every corner of the world to the institution
at 183rd Street and Third Avenue in the Bronx, New York.
Once called the St. Barnabas Hospital for Incurables, it is
today a far from hopeless place for many of its patients.

More than ten thousand patients here and many thousands
more around the world have been given relief from crippling
neurologic diseases through surgical techniques developed by
Dr. Irving Spencer Cooper.

The athletic, blond neurosurgeon is prodded by a compelling drive to help the presumably hopeless. He has seen
more than most of human suffering, and has done more than
most to alleviate it. Cooper has to his credit more significant
innovations in brain surgery than any of his contemporaries,
perhaps more than any man who has ever lived.

Yet there was little in Cooper's early life that would portend
what was to come. In fact he started the road to medicine
because of an experience another kind of person might have
forgotten.

The summer after his first year in college he had returned
home to Washington, D.C., to work as a delivery boy for a
small grocery and meat market in the Northwest section of
the city. He enjoyed his deliveries in this rather middle-class
neighborhood. As the last day of work arrived young Cooper

mentioned to one of his customers that he was returning to school.

"What will you study?" she asked.

"I think I'm going to go to law school," he replied.

"Oh, no. You shouldn't go to law school. You look just like a doctor."

Exactly the same dialogue took place at his next two deliveries. And when the teen-ager returned home to his mother's apartment he proclaimed, "I think maybe I'll study medicine."

He had made the statement only partly in good faith, for deep inside he still believed that he wouldn't be able to dissect animals or look at blood without feeling faint. To test himself, he signed up for as many scientific courses as he could during his sophomore year.

The blood and bugs didn't bother young Cooper as much as he had imagined they might, and his pursuit of a medical education began. He entered the George Washington University Medical School in 1941. His first, long-lasting love affair began that very year. It was with the human brain.

"I was studying neural anatomy. I loved what appeared to be the logic of the various nervous pathways, of the sensation coming into the nervous system through a specific receptor and going along certain pathways and being interpreted in the brain. Ultimately it all helped to make a complex personality. The profundity of the organ, the fact that life really existed in the brain. It soon became apparent to me that you are your brain."

Cooper's professor of neurology and neural anatomy was Dr. Walter Freeman, the man who introduced the prefrontal lobotomy operation. In those days, before tranquilizers and other drugs, the lobotomy was the only way to relieve certain severe mental disorders. Freeman performed the operation using an ice pick.

As dramatic in the lecture hall as he was in the operating

room, the professor thrilled Cooper when he rushed to the blackboard, a piece of chalk in each hand, and drew cross-sections of the brain using both hands simultaneously—each producing an exact mirror image of what the other hand was doing and both coming together to produce a graphic representation of the entire cross-section.

United States medical schools condensed their programs to a solid two years and eight months of study because of the nation's need for doctors during and immediately after World War II. After graduation Cooper did a double-duty internship, also serving as a naval medical officer at the US Naval Hospital in St. Albans, Long Island. He spent his last five months of duty aboard the tanker *USS Passumpsik*. Seasick the entire voyage, Cooper lost forty pounds, but managed to feed his hunger for literature by reading two books a day. Later he combined his love for both literature and neurology in a paper on the medical aspects of the death of Desdemona.

In the early spring of 1946 Cooper was assigned to the neurological service of Dr. Thomas Hoen, who one day arranged for his staff to visit the Montefiore Hospital in the Bronx.

Montefiore in those days was primarily a chronic-disease hospital, and its neurological wards were like medical museums, crammed with the victims of every conceivable chronic, incurable, neurologic disease the young doctors could imagine. Chief of that service was Dr. Houston H. Merritt, and it was Merritt himself who conducted the tour.

It is ironic that Merritt, who later became one of Cooper's greatest critics, first introduced him to at least one of the conditions Cooper would later alleviate—dystonia musculorum deformans.

"On that day I saw a ward of twisted, thrashing, deformed, writhing bodies, totally bedridden," Cooper recalls. "There was no known treatment for this disease of abnormal postures and involuntary movements, and the patients in this human zoo could do nothing for themselves. There was no known treatment or evidence that the disease could ever be reversed."

None of the doctors or patients present that day could know that within ten years Cooper would carry out the first successful treatment of a dystonic patient. And there was no reason why even Cooper himself should show more than a passing interest, for in those days he was primarily interested in paraplegics, a problem especially pressing during war years.

In 1948 Cooper was accepted as a fellow in neurosurgery at the famed Mayo Foundation in Rochester, Minnesota. Here the young neurosurgeon became something of a legend for his work habits. He carried out more clinical research than any neurosurgical fellow they had ever had up to that time. His appetite for knowledge of the human brain was voracious. He spent every spare moment in the library. The librarian gave him a private room in which to study.

Now Cooper became almost a recluse. When he wasn't studying in the library he locked himself in the attic of the little house where he and his wife lived in Rochester. When guests dropped by he often even begged off emerging for a "hello." He had to study, to learn, to teach himself. He also insisted on making time to spend with his family.

Cooper conveyed his love for books to his children. When his first son, Dan, was two years old Cooper started teaching him to read, and the boy did quite well. One day the proud father had his son demonstrate his abilities to a fellow neurosurgeon.

"Christ, Coop," said the friend. "Stop that. You'll make a freak out of the kid."

Concerned at the possibility, Cooper stopped the lessons. Dan, however, continued reading on his own, and a couple of years later, after the Coopers had moved to a New York

THE LIFE GIVERS

suburb, the family went to a local hotel for a Sunday brunch. As the waiter passed out menus, four-year-old Dan picked one up and ordered.

A man at the next table was startled by the little fellow reading a menu. He leaned over and said, "Say there, sonny. Where in the world did you ever learn to read?"

Dan returned the look and haughtily replied: "I teached myself."

After his Mayo Clinic Fellowship, Cooper moved to New York, where he had the opportunity to work with Howard Rusk at his rapidly growing Institute of Rehabilitation Medicine at New York University. Cooper also became an assistant professor of surgery at NYU Medical School and divided his time between working with paraplegics at Rusk's Institute and doing general brain surgery at NYU's Bellevue Hospital.

One morning in October, 1951, Cooper, now twenty-nine, and two of his junior residents in neurosurgery entered a Bellevue operating room. The object of their intentions was Joseph Cioppa, a forty-year-old truck driver from Philadelphia, whose right side had begun to shake uncontrollably ten years before. At first the tremor was almost imperceptible, but the shaking had gradually increased until Cioppa could no longer work at his job or even use his right hand to feed himself. He could, in fact, no longer do very much at all without help. He was condemned to live the remainder of his life as the prisoner of his own muscles.

Cioppa's symptoms were quickly recognized by the doctors as those first described in 1817 in an essay called "On the Shaking Palsy," by James Parkinson, an English physician. It was a syndrome, he wrote, ". . . of nature highly afflictive. . . . The unhappy sufferer has considered it as an evil, from the domination of disease which he had no prospect of escape."

The operation Cooper was to perform on Joseph Cioppa was a risky one. Everybody in the room knew that, including the patient. The surgeon was to cut the motor pathway in Cioppa's midbrain, thus swapping his Parkinsonian tremor for a partial paralysis of the affected side of his body. It would be a high price to pay, but Cioppa and his physicians knew that even a partial paralysis would be better than the constant involuntary movements that tortured his every waking hour. They were movements from which "he had no prospect of escape."

Assisted by residents Laurence Levy of England, and Aldo Morello of Italy, Cooper opened the patient's skull just in front of his ear and separated the membranes that covered the brain. Ever so gently, the temporal lobe of the truck driver's brain was lifted so the midbrain could be seen.

The surgeons noticed that due to an earlier illness, perhaps encephalitis or another kind of brain infection, part of the membrane covering Cioppa's midbrain adhered to it in an unnatural way. Cooper had to separate the membrane with some extra dissection, gently and deftly, with forceps and scalpel. In the tricky process a tiny artery deep within the brain was accidentally nicked. It bled profusely—so much, in fact, that the surgeon believed the patient's very life to be in grave danger. He asked Dr. Morello to go down to the waiting family and tell them the operation had taken an ominous turn.

Soon, though, with a tiny silver surgical clip Cooper was able to control the bleeding, and he went ahead with his dissection. As he worked he began to think about that esoteric little artery he had inadvertently ruptured. He worked quickly, quietly, his glove-covered hands caressing Cioppa's naked brain. And to this task he devoted 100 percent of his thought and energy. But even as he did, in the depths of his mind he was quickly, systematically reviewing every relevant piece of medical literature he had ever seen.

What is that little artery? Where does it go? What does it do?

It must be, he decided, the anterior choroidal artery. Its functions had been largely unknown until very recently. Cooper recalled a recent article that reported this tiny vessel irrigated the globus pallidus and portions of the thalamus, structures in the center of the brain that were thought to be linked to regulation of motor activity.

An accident had occurred. A lucky accident, perhaps, but as Louis Pasteur once noted, "Chance favors the prepared mind." If Cooper had not been prepared he might have continued the operation that was meant to paralyze half of Joseph Cioppa's body. If he had you would not be reading this story. But Cooper had another idea. He would end the operation before cutting the midbrain as planned and find out what effect the closing of the anterior choroidal artery would have. Assisted by Dr. Levy, he closed the wound in Cioppa's head and waited.

Serendipity smiled later that day. When the patient awoke from his anesthetic sleep his Parkinsonian tremor and rigidity had disappeared—without subsequent paralysis or effect on speech or any other motor functions. In fact the only difference that Cooper and his colleagues could determine in Cioppa's condition was the absence of the disabling tremor. Was this a miracle?

Twenty years and thousands of patients later a reporter watched Cooper perform a dramatic operation on a Parkinson's disease patient. "It's miraculous," the reporter commented as the patient's palsied hand stopped shaking.

"No miracle," reprimanded the neurosurgeon. "We doctors are people, not gods. We do our best, but that's all we can do."

Time and again Cooper and his associates examined Joseph Cioppa. Would his tremor return that night, the next day, the next week? It did not. Cooper phoned Dr. Fred Mettler, professor of neuroanatomy at the Columbia University College of Physicians and Surgeons. Mettler, a meticulous student of the brain, had done considerable experimental work in involuntary movement disorders, and young Cooper needed the benefit of his knowledge and experience.

"I didn't know him, had never met him, but asked if I could come up and visit him," Cooper recalls. "I told him what I had done and what had happened, and he arranged for me to operate on a couple of baboons at Columbia."

Cooper was already asking himself the question: Could a purposeful occlusion of this little artery routinely relieve the tremor and rigidity of Parkinsonism in humans? Or was Joseph Cioppa's operation some kind of freak incident, never again to be repeated?

After the baboons recovered from surgery they were sacrificed, and Mettler looked into their brains to see which tissue had been destroyed by cutting off the blood flow through the anterior choroidal artery. Mettler's careful studies of the baboon brains strengthened Cooper's fledgling hypothesis that his earlier accident had indeed damaged the structures in the brain that contributed to the tremor mechanism.

The key structure affected was the thalamus, a walnut-sized island in the center of the brain. The thalamus is a type of communications center, interpreting sensory information from the muscles, eyes, ears, and skin. When the thalamus receives or distributes garbled information, due to a kind of static within the body, contortions and uncontrolled movements can occur.

When Irving Cooper gets a promising idea he becomes obsessed with it. It burns within him like a fierce flame, consuming his every thought and action until the idea bears fruit or can be discarded. And he became obsessed with the possibility of relieving the tremors of Parkinsonism without paralyzing the patient, just as a dozen or more years before he had been obsessed with making the football team at Atlantic City High School. Making the varsity team had excited young Cooper so much that when he was put down to the second team he brooded for days.

And football was only a game. This was the real thing, for the biggest stakes—human life. After all, there were a million or more victims of this shaking palsy in the United States alone. Many other diseases of the central nervous system produced similar, disabling, and bizarre involuntary movements. In the past half-century these symptoms had led victims to all kinds of experimental brain operations in the hope of achieving a modicum of relief.

Thus far, of course, Cooper was still dealing with little more than an accident with fortuitous results, and a relatively small—but still significant—body of facts that seemed to support his hypothesis. His theories, however, were contrary to everything his more experienced colleagues believed. The only others who could really comprehend what had happened were the two doctors who themselves had watched. When other colleagues were told about the experience, many would simply not believe it.

The twenty-nine-year-old had to make a crucial decision. Would he drop it all, believe the neurologists and surgeons who said that the only way to relieve the Parkinsonian tremors was to partially paralyze the patient? Or would he put more faith into what he had seen, what he alone had learned, and attempt to close off the anterior choroidal artery of another Parkinson's disease victim? This time he would do it with the deliberate intent of trying to halt the tremors.

Unbeknownst to Cooper it hadn't been many months before that a young medical scientist in Pittsburgh had a similar dilemma in a totally different medical field. But Jonas Salk did not give up on the idea of a killed virus polio vaccine, even though the leading lights of bacteriology and virology said that only a live virus vaccine could give immunity. Neither did Walt Lillehei, in Minneapolis, back away from his conviction that he could successfully repair defects deep within a living human heart, in spite of prevailing surgical "wisdom" to the contrary. From Howard Rusk, Cooper had heard personally how difficult it can be to establish radical new ideas in the medical world.

In the face of their critics, Salk, Lillehei, Rusk, and more like them pursued their goals—and succeeded brilliantly. So, too, did Irving Cooper. He combed the three medical institutions he attended as a neurosurgeon, seeking suitable patients for his first deliberate try at relieving the tremors of Parkinson's disease.

The right patient would have to be very seriously disabled to accept the dangers inherent in such a tricky new procedure. Yet he or she would also have to be in relatively good health otherwise to qualify as a good surgical risk.

One of the hospitals Cooper attended was the Central Islip State Hospital, sixty miles from Manhattan, in Long Island. He visited this state hospital for mental diseases every week or so, mainly to perform psychosurgical operations such as lobotomies on the mental patients. "This was all we had to offer those patients at the time," Cooper recalls. "Once we had the tranquilizer drugs I gave up that kind of work."

Cooper found Bill Tremaine (not his real name) in one of the back wards of Central Islip.

"He was thirty-eight years old, totally bedridden, shaking violently, drooling, expressionless, almost speechless. He had been in the hospital about eight years. His Parkinsonism began following encephalitis eighteen years ago. For the past eight years he had been totally bedridden and incapacitated. He was admitted to the state hospital after a suicide attempt and he continued to deteriorate.

"We got hold of his sister, his closest living relative, and explained that we had this new idea, and asked for permission to perform this operation on Bill, and we got it."

So Cooper, with his resident Aldo Morello, brought Tremaine into the operating room at Central Islip State Hospital and opened his skull. The operation was uneventful, and afterward Cooper made the sixty-mile return trip to Manhattan, leaving Morello in charge of the patient, who was still unconscious from the surgical anesthetic.

The next morning Cooper left home early so he could get back to Central Islip State for a consultation with another patient. Aldo Morello ran to greet him in the corridor.

"Come! Look in here. We have got a Nobel prize waiting in this room." (Actually, neither Cooper nor any other of the Life Givers have received Nobel prizes as of this writing, although several have been considered.)

Cooper entered and saw Bill. He was awake and had no tremor or rigidity on the side opposite the side of the brain that had been operated. "Not only that, but he could already get out of bed and walk," Cooper recalls.

For the first time a patient had been deliberately cured of a symptom of Parkinsonism without being paralyzed in exchange. Once it had been done by accident. But now it had all been planned, and the man was already out of bed and walking.

"I took movies of him doing pushups just days after the operation. When I showed those movies at a medical meeting shortly thereafter," Cooper recalled, "doctors there got up and hollered 'fraud.' They just couldn't believe or accept it."

But whether or not anyone else chose to believe it, Bill Tremaine could walk. The man was so elated he hardly knew what to do with himself. So he borrowed nickels. Nickels?

Clutching a coin in his hand, he put on his well-worn bathrobe and walked to the end of the hospital corridor. There he put a nickel in the Coke machine. He did it twenty or thirty times a day. Bill borrowed nickels from anybody who came close enough for him to ask.

One day while discussing the case with Cooper, Morello,

the Italian resident, burst into tears. "You know," he said, "this is like one of the characters in a novel I read once. He had been in prison for all his life and was suddenly paroled. When he got home he kept walking back and forth over the threshold of his own door to show himself that he could really do it."

As time went by Cooper eventually operated on Tremaine two more times to relieve the tremors of his other side. Soon Bill could go home on weekends, and later he was discharged. He got a job as a plumber's assistant and earned his own living.

"For a long time Bill used to write to me. About 1959 or so when Margaret Bourke-White wrote a story about her Parkinson's disease operation in *Life* magazine I got a note from Bill, which I still have in his chart. He wrote, 'Dear Dr. Cooper, I hope you realize how famous I've made you over the years and I wonder if you could do two things for me. Could you buy me a television set? And send me about $50 a week spending money?'"

Cooper performed his operation on a score more patients, and in June, 1953, he traveled to Atlantic City to deliver a paper to the American Neurological Association. Its subject was the relief of the tremor and rigidity of Parkinsonism in man by occlusion of the anterior choroidal artery.

The paper was brief. "It was a good paper," Cooper recalled. "A concise report which I had memorized, and gave without any notes. It was my impression from the applause that it was very well received, and I was besieged by men congratulating me after the presentation."

There were, however, those who did not think young Cooper deserved congratulations. One elderly neurologist stood in the corridors outside the lecture hall and told a group of physicians that Cooper's report just couldn't be true, that the young neurosurgeon was exaggerating.

After all, the same year Joseph Cioppa had been operated

on at Bellevue, the editor of the *Yearbook of Neurology, Neurosurgery, and Psychiatry* had written that "Involuntary movements can be relieved only by substituting paralysis for the involuntary movement, and neurosurgery seems to have no application in this broad field."

There were some physicians, however, who weren't bound by preexisting prejudice and believed Cooper's reports. When he returned from Atlantic City one of the neurology professors at Cornell University Medical School who had heard his presentation phoned to ask if Cooper would come to the New York Hospital to examine Dr. Richard Young, professor of neurology at the University of Nebraska. Young, at the time, was totally incapacitated and bedridden due to Parkinsonism.

"Since I had operated on so few patients by the anterior choroidal technique, and knowing it to be both new and investigative and hazardous, it seemed a welcome opportunity to me, because I thought that doctors, particularly neurologists, who could understand the risks involved, and knew what their disease meant, would be best able to make a judgment as to whether to have such a new and hazardous and unknown operation. So I went, at the invitation of Dr. Henry Dunning, to see Dr. Young."

Cooper was surprised to see how severely incapacitated the Nebraskan neurologist really was. Violent tremors in all four limbs literally shook his entire bed. As Cooper entered the hospital room Young said, "Well, so you are the young miracle man I've been looking for."

Cooper then sat beside the professor's bed and told him about the new operation.

"By that time," Cooper said, "I'd done only twelve cases. There had been one mortality and two patients had suffered from hemiplegia [paralysis of one side], but seven of the cases had had spectacular results. We had clearly demonstrated that tremor and rigidity could be relieved without paralyzing the patient. One of the patients, Bill Tremaine, had already gone more than a year without a recurrence of symptoms."

Dr. Young asked Cooper to operate. Several other physicians were consulted and decided that the degree of the man's helplessness definitely made him a candidate for the operation.

It was performed, and Cooper put the tiny silver clip on Young's anterior choroidal artery. The ailing physician responded well to the surgery. The tremor and rigidity on one side of his body disappeared, and he could freely move his limbs. Everyone was elated—so elated that a week later it was decided that Cooper would perform the same operation on the opposite side of the brain in order to relieve the symptoms of the other half of Dr. Young's body.

This time, however, problems arose. Young became comatose after the operation; he developed pneumonia.

"After several days of moribund condition on the part of Dr. Young, his physician-brother, unbeknownst to me, called Dr. Houston Merritt, who had been a classmate of Dr. Young in medical school, and the great professor came to see Dr. Young in my hospital in consultation. I received no telephone call from Dr. Merritt for information about the case and did not have the privilege of being present at the time of the consultation.

"However, the following day when I made rounds I was informed by the patient's brother that he wished the intravenous feedings stopped. I was further informed that Merritt had been there and had told him that it had been ridiculous to undertake that surgery in the first place, since tremor and rigidity could not be relieved by neurosurgical means and that the only way to relieve tremor and rigidity was by paralyzing the patient.

"He stated, therefore, that since the patient's condition was so critical it would be best to discontinue the futile attempts to keep him alive. About three weeks later Dr. Richard Young died.

"I spent those three weeks, day and night, in the hospital, almost always under the surveillance of an angry, hostile family and under the indictment of having performed an op-

eration that had no chance anyway. But in the hospital at the
same time was Wayne Dorset [not his real name], whose
tremor and rigidity had been totally relieved by the operation.
Furthermore, the surgery had also reversed a dystonic deformity in one of his hands."

Wayne had had his operation in September, 1953. The
morning after surgery the tremor and rigidity of his left ex-
tremities had been totally relieved. Within a few days he could
walk for the first time in more than ten years. Most surprising,
however, was the reduction of the deformity in Wayne's left
hand, which seemed to be due to the loosening of some of the
muscles that had previously flexed his wrist.

Originally it had been thought that this deformity, similar
to deformities caused by a neuromuscular disease of children
called dystonia musculorum deformans, was irreversible and
due to bone, muscle, and tendon deformities. Two months
after his surgery, however, it was found that Wayne's dystonic
deformity had totally vanished as a result of the relief of muscular rigidity on that side. Thus it was learned that this type
of deformity was really an abnormal posture, without permanent fixation, and potentially reversible.

So, notwithstanding two surgical deaths and flaring medical
controversies, two years after his serendipitous discovery,
Cooper had shown that the anterior choroidal artery occlusion
could reverse not only the tremor and rigidity of Parkinsonism,
but could ease other spastic deformities as well.

But the skepticism over his techniques began to eat at
Cooper, who couldn't understand why many of his colleagues
simply refused to believe what he had shown to be true beyond
doubt. It was this constant criticism that drove him, almost
fanatically, to document every single one of his cases. To do so
he has amassed an incomparable film library of neurological
disorders consisting of more than a million feet of film. Over
the years Cooper also took cues from his friend Howard Rusk
and frequently brought patients to medical meetings. His col-

leagues might not like what he said, but when he could produce flesh-and-blood results they had to pay attention.

With the pressure of continually being in the center of controversy, it's no wonder that previous inconveniences became intolerable to Cooper. One of these was the working conditions at Bellevue Hospital.

He had, after all, come from the famous Mayo Clinic, known as much for its kindness and compassion as Bellevue was for its indecent inhumanity. "I saw patients come into Bellevue and lie thirty, forty, or fifty days before anybody would examine them. If all they needed was a fairly simple test they might be there three months and cost the city four thousand dollars. We had one nurse for two forty-bed wards, and I felt that I just couldn't do any more work there."

The only answer, he felt, was to leave New York. So Cooper went to Howard Rusk, "a kind of a father figure to me at the time," and told him that he had to find another place to work. "I just can't work under these conditions at Bellevue. And I know that this Parkinson's thing is true, so I'm going to start looking around the country to see where I can go and work."

Rusk urged him to wait. Before moving away from New York, he said, Cooper ought to look into a hospital in the Bronx, then called the Home for Incurables. Rusk had some contact with the hospital, having sent a rehabilitation consultant there, and had been told that the administrators wanted to start making the hospital a bit more dynamic.

"You really ought to go up and have a talk with them," Rusk urged. When Cooper did, the superintendent of the place pointed out that his institution had no real operating facilities. He would, however, be willing to supply Cooper with a small room on the third floor.

That room was tiny—about twelve by fifteen feet. But it was in this improvised surgical area that Cooper, assisted by one doctor and one nurse, performed his first one thousand operations at St. Barnabas. Since fancy hospital equipment wasn't available in the new operating room a kitchen chair was used to sit up the Parkinson's disease patients for surgery. Later a barber's chair was substituted.

Cooper went to St. Barnabas in September, 1954, with the idea of operating Saturdays only, one or two cases a week, and continuing his own work at NYU. By that time he had been made a full professor and was hopefully awaiting the establishment of a neuromuscular institute which he would head.

The first operations Cooper and Aldo Morello performed at St. Barnabas met with tremendous success—and it was a good thing, because Cooper later learned that if any of those first operations had failed and a patient had died, the administrator at St. Barnabas had decided he would no longer let Cooper operate there. But that never came to pass, and Cooper's practice at St. Barnabas continued to grow, as did his reputation.

But even though the anterior choroidal artery operation continued to be effective in relieving the tremor and rigidity of Parkinsonism Cooper felt it was still too hazardous. One reason for this is that the brains of different people are no more similar than their noses or chins. Each is different in its own way. And sometimes that tiny artery called the anterior choroidal would go here, at other times it might just go there; thus, occluding it could cause a bit too much tissue damage—or too little. It just wasn't a procedure that could be sufficiently relied upon even though the statistics for the operation were encouraging. The feasibility of this type of surgery had definitely been proven, but it left something to be desired. There was a mortality rate of 10 percent and a serious complication rate of another 10 percent. After Cooper had performed the operation on fifty-five patients he decided to seek a safer method. He would work on a way of directly destroying the target tissue, rather than relying on occluding the artery which, in turn, would cause tissue death.

Absolute alcohol injected carefully into certain areas of the brain would kill the tissue, he reasoned. But he wondered how he would be able to determine just where the correct area was. Some kind of a test was needed.

"If only," Cooper thought, "I could temporarily deaden the guilty portion of the brain and test the patient's reaction. Then I could operate with more certainty than ever before."

He devised just such a test by injecting procaine, a local anesthetic, into the portion of the globus pallidus that he was aiming to destroy. If the patient's Parkinsonian tremor and rigidity were eased without signs of paralysis, Cooper would then drip in absolute alcohol to permanently destroy the tissue.

This procedure pushed Cooper even further from classical brain surgery of the time, for in this new operation the patient had to be awake so he could cooperate with the neurosurgeon as tests for paralysis were made.

Pain was not a problem, since local anesthesia could easily deaden the area of the skull where incisions had to be made; and the human brain itself is actually insensitive to physical pain.

After using his new technique for a while Cooper found that the procaine used to test would sometimes spread, giving false and unreliable results. So he developed a probelike tube with a tiny inflatable balloon at the end. By inserting the tube and blowing up the balloon, certain cells would be squeezed, thus blocking their activity and abolishing the tremor and rigidity if placed at the proper location. The tiny inflated balloon also made a cavity into which the absolute alcohol could be injected.

Cooper and his colleagues continued to explore the entire region of the brain affected by these new operations. Using sophisticated electronic gear they systematically tested different areas of the globus pallidus and the nearby thalamus, near the center of the brain. By changing the target of his surgery from the globus pallidus to the thalamus itself, he improved the predictability of results.

Whereas Cooper rejoiced in his success, many of his eminent neurosurgical colleagues did not. It is probably fair to say that Cooper's thalamic procedures were among the most controversial brain operations ever. The infighting among the neurologists and neurosurgeons was fierce—and often fiercely personal.

In the early spring of 1956 Cooper received in his office mail a small booklet of abstracts of papers to be presented at that year's annual meeting of the American Academy of Neurology. Thumbing through them, he noticed a paper by the renowned professor of neurology at Columbia University's College of Physicians and Surgeons, Dr. Houston Merritt.

Cooper was surprised to read in Merritt's paper that he—the most influential neurologist in America at the time—contended that there was no way to relieve tremor and rigidity by surgery without paralyzing the patient. In those cases in which the tremor or rigidity had disappeared, Merritt said, it was invariably due to a motor weakness and that the symptoms occurred when the power reappeared in the patient's limbs.

By this time five years had elapsed since Cooper's initial discovery, and he had reported on more than three hundred surgical cases of Parkinsonism relieved by his methods.

"I had absolute proof that one could relieve tremor and rigidity without paralyzing the patient. I wrote to Merritt repeating this, but I received no reply.

"Finally I got in touch with Dr. Robert Schwab at Harvard, who had been examining all of our cases. I asked him to read the abstract. I told him of my attempt to reach Dr. Merritt. Dr. Schwab was able to do just that. He wrote him, suggesting as tactfully as he could that it would be wise for Merritt to come visit me and examine some of our cases before going to that meeting in St. Louis.

"Dr. Merritt finally came one Saturday, and he and a couple of assistants spent all day with me. I presented to him twenty patients I had operated on, all of whom had been through his own clinic first. I showed him films of each patient and he just sat there puffing his pipe and left without saying anything. But when the St. Louis meeting came he did pull back from the hard line he had taken originally and said there was an indication that some patients could be helped by surgery."

Operations as dramatic and successful as Cooper's, coupled with his forceful personality and good looks, made fantastic newspaper and magazine copy. But since both Cooper and his work had been subject to so much controversy and criticism he became hypersensitive about publicity. One person he turned to was Dr. Iago Galdston. Blunt in speech, occasionally profane, Galdston, a psychiatrist, was also permanent secretary of the New York Academy of Medicine. One area he handled concerned publicity, screening of medical items that might get into the press. He held that position when Cooper reported his earliest Parkinsonism work.

"When it received so much publicity, and I was so widely criticized by my colleagues," Cooper said, "I used to run to Dr. Galdston for advice as to what to do, since I was not seeking the publicity and I would often literally hide when reporters came to seek me out."

Eventually Galdston got tired of Cooper's visits after every little peep from the press or from colleagues irate over one thing or another.

"Look, Cooper," Galdston scolded, "you're a maverick and you're a pioneer. If you don't want any criticism, well, just don't do anything new. If you want to do anything new, then you'll just have to tell all those old birds to go screw themselves."

Cooper, noted novelist C. P. Snow, "attracts some envy, presumably because he appears to have all the gifts that a man might conceivably wish for." Indeed, Cooper was young, aggressive, brilliant. He lived his own life. In the mid-1950s, for example, he bought himself a boat and used it to commute to work at the NYU Medical Center.

And when those pipe-smoking "old birds" known as academicians saw the neurosurgeon who looked like a football halfback get off his pleasure craft that had just sped down the foam of the East River, jump over the fence and rush off to teaching rounds or surgery . . . well, they detested him even more. It was that simple.

"I used to get up and walk around the streets at night," said Cooper. "Some nights I'd get into my car. I thought, Jesus, maybe I'm insane. Here are all these people. . . . I keep going to meetings where I can't even get on the program, and they're having a discussion of anterior artery occlusion, the operation I discovered.

"And on the program are four different people who have each done a single case, and they all failed. So they say it obviously doesn't work. And I'm sitting right there, having done more than all of the people in the world combined, and couldn't even get on the damn program.

"At night I started thinking about it. 'Maybe they are right,' I would think. 'After all, they've been neurosurgeons for twenty or thirty years.' So I'd get in my car and drive out to Central Islip—seventy miles at two o'clock in the morning. And I'd wake up a patient and make him walk around and look at him. I had to do it just to convince myself again— you know, to give me faith for another week."

Cooper continued to question himself and his methods. He continued to revise, improve, perfect. And over the next few years he performed thousands of operations, most of them to relieve the symptoms of Parkinson's disease. Constantly combining surgery with research, always seeking to improve his technique and the relief he was able to give to patients.

The Cooper family exchanged presents beneath the Christmas tree in their Westchester County home as usual on Christmas morning in 1960. There were books, records, and plenty of toys for little Doug and Dan and Lisa.

Their mother was pleased with the lovely gifts her family

had chosen for her. As for Father . . . well, the Cooper family faced an old dilemma. What is a good Christmas present for a wealthy, world-renowned doctor—the proverbial man who has everything?

How about the latest mechanical gadget? Irving Cooper had always adored contraptions, thought his wife, so she bought him a new kind of wine-bottle opener, the kind that opens a bottle by shooting a charge of carbon dioxide via a hypodermic-like needle pushed through the cork. The increased air pressure inside the bottle forced the cork to pop right out. He tried it, and it worked. But it was the frosty ring that the opener left inside the bottle's neck that fascinated Cooper most. For hours as he sat relaxing that Christmas Day he remained fascinated, fiddling with the bottle opener. He shot tiny jets of icy carbon dioxide at his hand and watched the effect.

"I played with that gadget for hours, freezing tiny areas on the palm of my hand and watching them thaw. What impressed me most was that I could control the area of freezing without overlapping into adjacent tissue. Why couldn't the same thing be done in the brain? After all, the tip of the opener looked something like a brain cannula. Then I got the idea of developing an instrument that would be a cannula, insulated on the sides, with a cooling tip that could be put into different parts of the brain."

Scores of animal experiments showed that the idea could work, and with engineers Cooper began to work out the technical details for a practical brain probe that could be brought to carefully controlled, subzero temperatures at its tip. He hired a couple of technician-engineers to work in his St. Barnabas laboratories to help perfect the instrument—dubbed a cryoprobe.

Soon Cooper began to collaborate with engineers at the Linde Division of Union Carbide, on a needlelike hollow tube through which liquid nitrogen—more efficient as a coolant than carbon dioxide—was pumped. The cryoprobe was designed so the temperature at the tip of the probe could be dropped as low as minus 196 degrees Centigrade, well below the temperature needed to freeze and kill human cells. Because of the way the length of the probe was protected by superinsulation, only its tip was cooled.

"When Union Carbide agreed to make the machine," Cooper recalled, "I said we would give them whatever we had. I had never applied for a patent and just gave them all of our equipment and information. In exchange I told them I wanted a grant to our research fund of two hundred thousand dollars. I also said I wanted to be able to give twelve machines to institutions around the world that I selected and taught how to use them. Then we would know the thing was not abused and was in good hands."

When the first machines, dubbed "Cooper Cryosurgery System," were ready, Cooper took a world tour to various medical centers where he gave away the twelve machines and lectured to colleagues on how to use them. To communicate more effectively on this and the many other trips abroad during his career, Cooper has hired language teachers to tutor him in the car going to and from work as well as during leisure time at home. In this way he learned to fluently speak five languages besides English.

While Cooper was traveling, explaining the new apparatus, two of the young men who had previously worked in his laboratory had secretly, and separately, applied for patents on the cryosurgery devices.

"The next thing I knew," Cooper recalls, "one kid instituted a million-dollar lawsuit for fraud against Union Carbide and me, for an infringement on his patent. When you are sued, you have to defend yourself—actually the hospital defended me. Naturally the case was thrown out of court, it never got anywhere. The whole story of my discovery was well-documented, my papers and my letters to the other people. Even if one of them did own the patent, I wasn't claiming to own anything, I wasn't selling it. I wasn't getting paid by Union Carbide.

"It was really driving my crazy. I had made an invention and had given it away. And all of a sudden here's an article in my local newspaper that I was fraudulent, and being sued for a million bucks.

"That lawsuit cost the hospital a thirty-five-thousand-dollar legal fee. The kid who was suing us didn't care. He kept getting various lawyers who would take his case on a percentage deal against me and Union Carbide. He figured that we'd settle for twenty-five grand apiece just to get off the hook. But we wouldn't do it. The case never even got to a deposition stage, the judge just threw it out. But it was really aggravating."

Cooper rapidly became known as the father of cryosurgery. He was glad to help other specialists broaden its applicability to diseases of other organ systems. The concept wasn't a new one, but the method and successful application were. It had been more than three hundred years before, that a British physician, Dr. Henry Power, froze tiny vinegar eels to see what effect the cold would have on their tissues. Already various chemicals had been used to freeze warts and other small skin growths so they could be removed. But those applications were scattered and met with varying degrees of success. It wasn't until Cooper's Christmas present in 1960, and his subsequent research, that cryosurgery as a practical medical tool came into its own. Today cryosurgery has not only been used to ease the tremors of Parkinsonism and the wretched spasms of dystonia and other functional movement disorders, but doctors around the world have successfully frozen away cataracts, ulcers, hemorrhoids, tonsils, prostate glands, and hundreds of types of tumors in most body locations.

It's doubtful that cryosurgery would have caught on so

quickly in such diverse medical specialties if it had not been used so successfully as a tool in brain surgery, particularly for Parkinson's disease.

Once, as he paused for a moment in the middle of an operation on a patient with Parkinson's disease, Cooper explained, "This is the point where the cryoprobe is uniquely suited to surgery for Parkinsonism. In it we have a controllable and reversible mechanism."

To illustrate his point, Cooper reaffirmed that the cryoprobe was in the proper place within the patient's brain and asked him to raise his hand. It trembled constantly. Now he asked that the probe's temperature be lowered to minus 10 degrees. Seconds later he asked the patient again to raise his right arm. The tremors were gone. Meanwhile other members of the operating team tested the patient's responses to make certain there were no untoward side effects and his sensory, motor, and intellectual functions remained normal.

"At minus 10 the temperature is cold enough to inhibit the function of the thalamus but not cold enough to destroy cells. If the patient's response hadn't been what we wanted we'd simply have raised the temperature, adjusted the probe, and tried again."

Cooper and his associates have found that cryosurgery is far safer and more precise than any other method. It has produced long-lasting relief from tremor and rigidity in 90 percent of good-risk patients. Poor risks, patients in their sixties and seventies with tremor on both sides and clear-cut impairments of their living activities, have a success rate of 60 percent.

In one study on 1,001 consecutive cases of patients who had received the freezing surgery for Parkinsonism, the St. Barnabas doctors found an overall mortality of 1.3 percent compared with the mortality rate of 2.3 percent in 1,000 cases of the operation in which parts of the brain were destroyed by chemicals.

Like so many brilliant technical innovations in the field of medicine and surgery, however, the cryothalamectomy procedures were rarely performed a dozen years after this discovery. The main reason was the discovery, in 1968, of the beneficial effect of a drug called L-dopa on Parkinsonism. Before the story of L-dopa's success was published, Cooper had learned about work on the drug done by Dr. George Cotzias of Brookhaven National Laboratory.

"I was so impressed by the effects of L-dopa that I put an immediate moratorium on surgery for Parkinson's disease and canceled seven hundred operations."

Those seven hundred patients, and others, participated in approved clinical trials of L-dopa at St. Barnabas.

"The only Parkinson's disease patients we operate on now," said Cooper in 1972, "are those who have had good L-dopa therapy in competent hands and whose tremor hasn't responded."

So just over a decade after the cryothalamectomy operation for Parkinsonism was pioneered at St. Barnabas, where up to one thousand patients a year were once operated on, only a few such procedures are performed each month.

"After having been an evangelist for this type of surgery for many years, I find that almost every other center is now doing more of it than we are."

The irony of this point is not lost on Cooper, who remembers too well the scorn many of these same physicians and centers once heaped on his discovery.

There were many times when Cooper's treatment of Parkinsonism was questioned because other surgeons could not reproduce his results. Some doctors simply refused to believe that the disease could be reversed without paralyzing the patient.

"Surgeons used to come here," Cooper recalled, "and watch us for a day or a couple of days and then go home and do the surgery. Some of them insisted on putting their patients to sleep. But you just can't tell if you are working in the right portions of the brain unless the patient is awake and you can see his response."

Some have questioned the propriety of Cooper's occasionally subjecting patients to radical procedures that have not first been perfected in animal experiments. One reason for that is there are no suitable animal models for many of the conditions being studied.

"We're talking about a patient," explained Cooper, "who has not just been sick for a week, but for years. Who is totally incapacitated, suffering both physically and mentally and willing to try anything. So I think that the criteria that I first put to myself is that what I'm about to suggest has as its sole thrust the therapy of that patient. Any question of new knowledge— although we are interested in it—is strictly a by-product."

Many of his patients *are* willing to try anything; some would quickly accept odds ten or twenty times the risk required for Cooper's surgery. And Cooper is keenly aware of the burden the desperation of these patients places upon him.

"They don't want to feel that you're unsure, that you're frightened. Even though you are. All the time."

In his 1973 book, *The Victim Is Always the Same,* Cooper described his own ethical-moral wrestling before he decided to operate on his first patient with dystonia musculorum deformans, a mercifully rare, inherited disease that sends children into progressively more violent contortions:

"How does one decide to place for the first time an instrument deep in a child's brain and destroy part of it? It's not a question of overcoming the technical difficulties, which can always be worked out in the laboratory. It's a more profound moral question than that, because only human beings have this disease," he wrote.

First described in 1908, dystonia came to be considered perhaps the most crippling and least curable of all the neurologic diseases. Genetic in origin, it can either be passed between generations or caused by specific genetic mutations. Ironically, the same collection of genes that carry dystonia seem also to carry a very high degree of intelligence, so its victims are abnormally bright and acutely aware of what is happening to them.

Recall Cooper's first look at a ward full of "twisted, thrashing, deformed, writhing bodies," in Montefiore Hospital back in 1946. And remember that early in his career Cooper had operated on a Parkinson's disease patient named Wayne Dorset. As a side effect of Wayne's operation, a long-standing dystonic deformity of his hands had been relieved.

Near the end of 1953 Cooper tested a hypothesis and became the first doctor to reverse and relieve dystonia's symptoms. He did it by destroying bits of tissue in the brain's thalamus, in almost exactly the same place he operated to relieve Parkinsonism. Relief of dystonia, however, was more difficult to achieve, and frequently as many as six or seven separate lesions were required.

The dystonia operations were also helped by cryosurgery, and in November, 1961, when twelve-year-old Miriam Kimmelman arrived at St. Barnabas Hospital in a wheelchair, she had some reason to be hopeful. She hobbled backward into Cooper's office, for that was the way her twisted legs propelled her with the least amount of pain. Miriam's body was twisted like a question mark. Indeed, in the three years since she began to feel the awful progression of dystonia, her whole life had become a question mark.

Problems first arose when Miriam's writing hand suddenly began to fling itself violently into the air, turning her schoolwork to "chicken scratches" and causing her classmates to snicker. What was happening?

Then her right foot started to drag, making the eight flights of stairs she had to climb every day a torture.

"I just had to walk," she said of that time, "because I just wasn't going to stay home." Eventually she negotiated the stairs and school corridors backward, always wracked with pain and well aware that "everyone was always staring."

It took a while for Miriam's family to find a doctor who could explain that she was suffering from dystonia. But it wasn't until September, 1961, that she had been given a hint that there might be help for her. The hint came from Joan Harris, once a victim of dystonia herself, who heard about Miriam and visited her to tell her and her parents about the recovery she made after Cooper's operation.

In January, 1962, Miriam was wheeled into the St. Barnabas operating theater. "I was crying—I was that happy," she recalled.

And when Cooper ordered the lowering of the temperature of his cryoprobe deep within Miriam's brain, she said, "I suddenly felt better. There I was lying—and all of a sudden I felt loose and not tired anymore. I felt it right up there," she said, gesturing toward her head, "so I was happy."

Progress came quickly for Miriam after her first operation, during which Cooper had deleted a small section of her left thalamus, the motor-control mechanism for the right side of the body, where Miriam had the most trouble.

Now the teen-ager was bombarding doctors, nurses, therapists, and family members with one question after another. "When can I have my other side done? When can I dance? When can I see Disneyland?"

Early in June she had a second operation. This time the surgeon destroyed a small area of her right thalamus to eliminate the symptoms still remaining on the right side.

Gradually all of Miriam's symptoms subsided. Within a few months she looked to be a normal thirteen-year-old, running, playing, once again able to compete in school.

More than ten years later the girl who had once hobbled backward into Cooper's office was still living a normal life.

Miriam's is not the only dramatic story among Cooper's long series of dystonic patients. Seventy-seven percent of them have shown long-term reversal of symptoms without sensory, motor, or intellectual impairment. In the rest of the cases, either surgery failed to reverse the symptoms or they later reappeared. The mortality rate has been 2.7 percent. And although Cooper won't use the word *cure*, many of his patients have been symptom-free for longer even than Miriam, and many are leading normal lives—some with children of their own.

It was in 1973, according to the *Journal of the American Medical Association*, that Cooper added "another bead—possibly the largest yet—to his string of achievements in 'functional neurosurgery.' "

The "biggest bead" is an ingenious device that seems to do for the brain what a pacemaker does for the heart—it delivers electrical impulses to the cerebellum and apparently modulates electrical activity. In many cases this brain pacemaker has stopped the disabling seizures of previously intractable epilepsy, reduced the spasticity of cerebral palsy victims, and eased the spastic paralysis that often follows a stroke.

In the first year and a half of his work on the cerebellar stimulator, Cooper had implanted the devices, with varying degrees of success, in about fifty patients. None of them had any adverse effects from the procedure which, unlike most brain operations, is not based upon destroying part of the brain itself.

Before the turn of the century British physiologist Sir Charles Sherrington found that stimulation of the anterior lobe of the cerebellum could ease decerebrate rigidity in cats. Fifty years later young Cooper, then doing his fellowship at the Mayo Clinic, read a report of the work of Italian physiologist Giuseppe Moruzzi. The report said Moruzzi had found that electrical stimulation of the cerebellum could inhibit or facilitate motion, depending on the frequency used.

"I made a note in the book," Cooper said, "that chronic

stimulation of the cerebellum in humans should relieve spastic states. I tried to work out the technology then, but couldn't. Later my other work kept me too busy."

Early in 1972 Cooper came across his earlier notation while preparing a lecture for students at the New York Medical College. "By that time I had more time for reflection, and new stimulators were available. So I began working on chronic stimulation of the brain."

Cooper's new operation consists simply of placing over the front and rear of the cerebellum the system's two sets of silicon-coated, Dacron-enmeshed electrodes. Wires are then run under the skin and down the neck to the chest, where two receivers are imbedded. Over this spot the surgeon tapes the antenna of a battery-powered radio transmitter the size of a cigarette pack. When activated the transmitter sends a small current through the cerebellum, an inhibitory part of the brain that functions somewhat like a rheostat and regulates certain of its activities.

"We theorize," Cooper said, "that cerebellar stimulation is modulating the central nervous system in these patients. The effect is different in each case; that is, activity (electrical stimulation) is corrected according to the patient's needs."

One of Cooper's former neurology professors at the Mayo Clinic, Reginald Bickford, later of the University of California, San Diego, confirmed that "this is very important work. I've talked to some of the patients and their relatives, and the effect is remarkable in epilepsy. It's possible not only to abort epileptic seizures, but unexpectedly this also seems to change the tendency even to have seizures. The surgery might also lead to research on drugs that accomplish the same thing. And it is important because it will tell us more about the brain."

The $3,000 brain-pacemaker system, which is still being improved upon, was conceived by Cooper and developed by him and a Long Island engineer. The electrician-father of one of Cooper's early pacemaker patients also designed a timing device to switch the transmitter's power on and off automatically at preset intervals. Cooper hopes that the entire system someday will be self-contained within the patient's body, as heart pacemakers already are. Since the brain stimulator uses about two hundred times as much power as the heart pacemaker, new power sources must be developed.

Although the early evidence on the brain pacemaker is extremely optimistic, especially for individuals suffering intractable epilepsy, it will be some years before firm conclusions can be drawn.

Some of Cooper's critics (although the pacemaker work has generally received immediate acceptance, in strong contrast to Cooper's earlier breakthrough developments) say that more carefully controlled operations on human beings must be undertaken before procedures such as the brain-pacemaker implantation can be considered effective. They have suggested double-blind testing in which, for example, out of one hundred patients fifty would receive working stimulators and the other fifty get "dummies." That approach is similar to using sugar pills in drug-efficacy studies.

Cooper asks: "What kind of controlled experiments can you do with these patients? You have to be honest with yourself and admit that you're working in a human situation and every case is different. In a drug study you can do a double-blind study. But you can't do that with the cerebellar stimulation. You can't open their heads and pretend to stimulate them.

"Any time you put a patient to sleep (stimulator-implant patients, unlike cryothalamectomy patients, must be put to sleep because of the nature of the surgery), you risk his life. Who could do that in good conscience and then not even try to help them? The risk so far outweighs the potential benefits to the patient that it would be absolutely immoral—and I would think illegal."

It's all a question of the surgeon's motives. Does he want

to help people, or does he want to make discoveries to embellish his record? If the latter were the case with Cooper, as some have indeed charged, the surgeon would have left the small Bronx hospital years ago for greener pastures, as various other surgeons frequently have done.

In fact in 1974 Cooper was offered a "package deal" of several million dollars to move his entire service from St. Barnabas to a new, private hospital outside New York City. "I am no football player," he confided to a friend. "I can't be bought and sold and traded."

Significantly, Cooper has worked essentially without government research grants during his professional career. The surgeon plows 20 percent of his own income back into his research, and St. Barnabas Hospital has contributed some $2 million in free patient care over the years.

"I'm convinced," Cooper says, "that motivation is an impossible thing to define. One thing that drives me is seeing someone who is sick and nobody else can help. That just upsets me and drives me harder."

But what of the responsibility? "It's standard to operate for brain tumors, and everyone knows that when you operate for a brain tumor, the patient may die. But if you're going to operate on something that's never been operated on before, your responsibility multiplies one thousand times. And if you're the type of person who identifies with the patient, you are agonized. It's not that you get an idea and come to peace with moral problems and then do it. You still have to cope with the people and their problems."

At a 1973 meeting of the American Neurological Association, Dr. William Sweet, professor of neurosurgery at Harvard University's Medical School, praised Cooper's pioneering work with the brain stimulator. But he added that it would have been a tough job to get any hospital research committee to approve such an original piece of work.

"That's a valid criticism," said Cooper. "One of the things

you have to start with, though, is that when you're dealing with humans, whatever you come up with is going to be imperfect and some of it will have to be judged after the fact. When you present people with so many things that are new, and some of them can't really be understood, you threaten their whole world. But you have to do it in the framework of the whole human problem."

Cooper adds, however, "If I had done ten cases and they all died, no matter how responsible I had been, it would have been wrong. You have the ultimate responsibility to yourself to be right. And if you aren't, you must find it out quickly."

In the brain-pacemaker work Cooper has not been wrong. Wayne Adams (not his real name), the first epileptic who received the system, is, two years after his operation, essentially seizure-free. This tall, handsome Nebraskan is now working with his physician, teaching other stimulator recipients how to care for and use their equipment.

For the four years before his November, 1972, operation, however, Wayne had been incapacitated by intractable epilepsy, apparently caused by a blow on the head from a baseball bat eight years earlier. He had full-blown seizures between one and five times a day, and another ten or fifteen times daily he had auras of nervousness and nausea. These symptoms, plus constant drowsiness caused by extraheavy but ineffective doses of anticonvulsive drugs, forced Wayne to drop out of college.

"When I'm faced with such a hopeless situation in a patient," Cooper said, "I'm driven to do something about it."

Today Wayne's medication has been cut to less than a fifth of its previous levels. Since surgery he has had several seizures, but all of them were linked to equipment malfunctions. Once a broken wire to the power source was discovered, and at other times, Wayne admits, "I let my battery go dead."

Another patient, a stroke victim who had suffered spastic paralysis on one side of his body for forty years, is, after the implant of a pacemaker, so loose he can walk without a cane.

Three weeks before her cerebellar stimulation began, a thirteen-year-old girl who had cerebral palsy was twisted like a pretzel, unable to utter more than a word or two. But only days after a cerebellar stimulator implant, she walked across the room unaided, laughing all the way.

Yes, there have also been some failures—patients whose conditions were not significantly improved by the stimulator. But it has been conclusively shown that electrical stimulation of certain areas of the brain can aid certain movement disorders.

"It's like a miracle, really," exclaimed Wayne Adams. "I can do just about anything I want now. I'm even going to get married. I have a good job here at the hospital helping new patients learn to use their stimulators and I'm going to school to learn more about electronics. In other words, I'm now leading a normal life except that I'm carrying the stimulator box around in my pocket."

Wayne is only one of many thousands of patients around the world who are indebted to Irving Cooper's pioneering success in controlling involuntary movement disorders through surgery—a mechanic has been returned to his tools, a doctor to his practice, a magician to his tricks. A lovely young girl, once grotesquely uncoordinated, is able to dance at her own wedding.

6 NATHAN KLINE:
Medicines for the mind

Nathan Kline likes to tell how he came into medicine through the back door. But a quick look around at the backgrounds of the other Life Givers shows that many of them entered the healing arts in similar ways.

Jonas Salk wanted to be a lawyer, Irving Cooper a man of law or letters. Walton Lillehei entered the pre-med course because he had to major in something and, after all, his father was a dentist. Perhaps there is a particular window on life that an individual can obtain if he or she, as Kline puts it, "doesn't start as a pre-med in kindergarten—the way many of my contemporaries did it."

In 1938 Nathan Kline was a poet, an English major at Swarthmore College. The summer before his freshman year he worked as a real estate salesman and while waiting around the office for customers he made his way through 105 books, including Aristotle's *Rhetoric*. This background enabled him to dispense with his college English requirements in two years, and he finished majoring in philosophy and psychology. Encouraged by a professor in graduate school, Kline went on to medical school.

By 1953 he had become a psychiatrist. While working at a huge state mental hospital he made a discovery that his contemporaries, a vast majority of his predecessors and, indeed, a good number of his successors were sure could not exist. His work marked a radical turning point in the treatment of the mentally ill. It opened an entire new discipline in psychiatry and led to new lives for millions of tortured human beings throughout the world.

In 1952 Kline left his job as director of research at Worcester State Hospital in Massachusetts and took a similar position at the Rockland State Hospital in Orangeburg, New York. At the time Rockland State was, except for its size, typical of most state mental institutions. With some 8,500 patients it was one of the largest, which meant mainly that the severity and scope of the usual problems were multiplied many times over.

Treatment for the mentally ill had come a long way by 1952. Though some believed that mental ailments were a product of the advances of civilization, man's troubled descriptions of the mentally ill actually appeared more than three thousand years ago. The Ebers Papyrus of 1550 B.C. describes a person whose ". . . mind raves through something entering from above."

Early treatment for mental illness ranged from trephining, or drilling a hole in the skull to let the demons out, to other forms of exorcising evil spirits. Chaining, beating, and various forms of bleeding were expected. Crude asylums and cruel isolation were the major "therapies" for the mentally ill for hundreds of years. In 1792 the famous French psychiatrist Dr. Philippe Pinel unshackled the institutionalized insane in Paris and promoted a more humane treatment for them. Through the 1800s there were other crusaders for reform in the treatment of the mentally ill. Best known, perhaps, was Dorothea Lynde Dix, whose lectures and lobbying were largely responsible for the establishment of large state mental hospitals in the United States.

By 1952—a century and a half after Pinel's monumental

strides—things were different. A little different, anyhow. You see, the scope of the problem was so large—in the mid-1950s there was a peak of more than 550,000 mentally ill hospitalized in the United States—that one in every two hospital beds was occupied by a mental patient.

Health professionals in psychiatric hospitals worked under constant personal danger. They were trained as therapists, but conditions forced them to function instead as guards and custodians, protecting patients from harming themselves or others.

Mental institutions—and Rockland State as much as any other—were still aptly described as "snake pits," hellish environments in which despair prevailed and a merciful death was often the only escape.

The wards of these mental hospitals were barren and bare. There were never drapes at the windows because they wouldn't last more than a single day. There were no rugs on the floor because the patients would urinate on them. Attendants had to take away shoelaces when patients came on the ward—for fear they would try to garrote somebody or hang themselves. Staff members often walked the wards in fear. It really did constitute a hazard at times; assaults were not at all that unusual. And it was not unknown for patients to be beaten up by attendants. Such actions were partly taken out of fear that if they didn't terrorize they were going to get it themselves.

Simply stated, the situation was ghastly. Compounding it all was the fact that there were few, if any, effective weapons the psychiatrists could enlist in their battle against mental diseases.

Large numbers of patients were kept in seclusion, restrained by heavy canvas straitjackets, or bound by sheets and doused with ice water; the resultant "wet packs" were among the most effective restraints ever contrived by man. Electric shock and insulin shock therapies were among the most common—and unappealing, not to mention potentially dangerous—forms of treatment for the chronic mentally ill. Debilitating lobotomy operations were becoming increasingly common. And there was little Howard Rusk-style rehabilitation for these patients—who lived in a stink and squalor far worse than most prisons—and their only crime, that they had the misfortune of having their illness settle in their minds instead of their lungs, their hearts, or their kidneys. The majority of those institutionalized were so deranged that they were beyond the reach of psychotherapeutic techniques being used by many psychiatrists in private practice.

With such conditions as the "norm" is it any wonder that the state mental hospitals were regarded far and wide as "the backwash of American medicine"?

All staff members at these institutions were grossly underpaid; the salary of the psychiatrists was incredibly low. This was only one other factor contributing to the reality that positions in the state hospitals were, more often than not, taken by doctors who simply couldn't get jobs elsewhere. Often they were foreign medical graduates unable to obtain licenses to practice privately, and the state hospitals were frequently the only openings they could take advantage of.

Why, then, did Nathan Kline accept the position at Rockland State Hospital—Nathan Kline, who had studied at Swarthmore, then continued at Harvard, Princeton, Rutgers, and the New York University School of Medicine?

The answer is relatively simple. Ever since he studied psychology at Harvard, no, even before, when he was a man of letters at Swarthmore, Kline had been fascinated by the age-old question of the possible relationship between mind and body. "Which is the psyche? Which the soma?"

The large state mental hospitals were, he says, "the only place where I could find the kind of patients in which I was interested. I wanted to observe the extreme examples—and they couldn't have been much more extreme than they were at Rockland State, a massive complex of gray-white buildings on the scenic west side of the Hudson River from New York City.

"You see," Kline observes, "one of the difficulties in studying the mind-body problem is that it is very difficult to distinguish between what is normal and what isn't normal. We accept things as 'givens,' so we never question them because there's no reason for it, so we often don't know what's important and what's not.

"So one of the best ways of studying behavior is doing it when it gets severely out of whack. Along the same lines, if you wanted to study watches but weren't allowed to open the cases, and if you just studied normally operating watches you wouldn't learn anything. But if you studied the watches that weren't working right, those going too fast, or too slow, or doing other things, you might begin to get some hint as to what was going on with this malfunctioning machinery. From that you could begin to put together a pattern of how those watches worked."

Kline's approach to mental illness was also greatly affected by his entry, in 1944, to the United States Public Health Service, which detailed him to the navy. There he was assigned to ships in the merchant marine—quite an educational experience for a budding psychiatrist. "In the merchant marine you saw so much pathology that if these people were not already working and doing a damn good job, you probably would have said they belong in a mental hospital."

It was here that Nathan Kline first learned that even some individuals with serious mental illness could continue, nevertheless, to make a useful contribution to society and get enjoyment out of life. "Just because they have some peculiar ideas is no reason to lock anybody up."

One of his seagoing patients was a black man who had been a cook for a quarter of a century. After the sailor had cleaned the galley every night he would go out onto the deck and talk to God.

"Now a lot of people do that," the psychiatrist notes, "but God talked back to this one. They used to have these conversations. So they sent the man to me because he was having auditory hallucinations. And I listened to him. There was no question but that he was paranoid, not that anyone was after him, but grandiose, and he was having these conversations he believed to be with God.

"They wanted me to discharge him, but I refused to go along with it. My point was that he had been doing this for twenty-five years and good cooks were hard to find. He wasn't doing anybody any harm. Well, they suspended him for a while, and we fought the thing out. It took three or four months, but they eventually let him go back to sea duty," Kline said.

But the real insanity of such situations, Kline told himself, was putting that kind of a person into a mental hospital in the first place. "He was making a living, a contribution, and wasn't doing anybody any harm. I don't even know if his problems even affected his own life. If he hadn't been hearing voices, I don't really know what difference it would have made. And we had no treatment at that time, so it just made no sense.

"The whole business of people functioning despite obvious mental illness was very important to me," Kline recalled.

Even from the very beginnings of his psychiatric research and clinical work Kline was not satisfied with the way his colleagues in the field had been going about treating the mentally deranged.

Late in 1952 he delivered a paper at the annual meeting of the American Association for the Advancement of Science. It foretold Kline's style, his interests, his fermenting discontent with the modus operandi of the psychiatric establishment. He said:

"Despite tremendous strides in the institutional care of

mental patients during the past twenty-five years, there has not been anything like a comparable advance in specific therapies or understanding of mental illness. This failure to produce new and significant information about causes and cures may be due in part to improper classification of the patients being studied rather than to unsuitable testing techniques. There exists a considerable body of evidence that seems to indicate that this is the case."

Then Kline proceeded to show the scientists in attendance the evidence—evidence indicating that psychiatrists, both clinical and research—simply had not been describing patients completely enough to determine very much at all about their state of health.

"Although," Kline continued, "the most convincing 'proof' that the present system is inadequate will be the substitution of a more productive one, the paucity of real progress despite promising leads suggests that the present classification may be the major deterrent."

This young psychiatrist wasn't going to let such problems spoil his research into the possible relationship between the mind and the body of his chronic mental patients. He kept voluminous records and did thousands of tests on those at Rockland State. He approached his patients' problems not just from the medical viewpoint but from the viewpoint of every discipline possible. This could be done, because at Rockland he had assembled a team of investigators with the "interest and skills of neuropsychiatrists, sociologists, psychologists, physiologists, endocrinologists, biometricians, biochemists, geneticists, anthropologists, statisticians, nurses, attendants, an electrical engineer, and a mathematical logician."

Making maximum use of this diverse team of professionals, Kline reported in 1952 that he hoped the procedures being established at Rockland would "ultimately make possible prediction of individual behavior under specified circumstances. . . . This, in turn, should stimulate techniques of control of human behavior (including the prevention and treatment of mental illness)."

By the time the above-quoted scientific paper—delivered in December, 1952—had been published in the *American Journal of Psychiatry* late in 1953, Nathan Kline and his Rockland team had opened the door to new "techniques of control of human behavior," to an extent so dramatic that there was hardly a way, even in his wildest imagination, that Kline could have projected the success when he wrote those somewhat naively optimistic words in 1952.

The research budget at Rockland State was quite small, and Kline's equipment for studying possible variables in the mind-body relationship was not at all elaborate. Sometimes he and his colleagues had to do without a particular piece of apparatus or use a makeshift, inadequate substitute, because funds for extensive research simply weren't available—especially at a state mental hospital.

To examine variables in the physical condition of mental patients, for example, Kline needed a Scholander apparatus, which measures the amounts of certain gases found in the blood. But the equipment cost one thousand dollars, and the money wasn't available.

One possible source of funds to make such a purchase could be a research grant from one of the large pharmaceutical firms. These were relatively common as "institutional grants" to various teaching and research hospitals. Far from pure charity, however, the firms that made such grants knew that they went a long way creating goodwill toward themselves and the brand names they produced.

"But nobody really gave a damn whether mental hospitals loved them or not at that time," Kline said, "because there were no drugs for the mentally ill, so we didn't do much

business with them anyway—they sold us a little phenobar-
bital, which we used as a sedative, and insulin that we used
for insulin shock therapy, but that was about it."

Thus hope for an institutional grant was pretty much eliminated, again the "aura" surrounding state mental hospitals
playing a major role. Some of the pharmaceutical firms, however, also gave out money for "product development grants."
But, added Kline, "that didn't make any difference either.
There were no drugs. Everybody knew there couldn't be any
drugs for psychiatric conditions."

And that would have been that . . . if Nathan Kline
weren't something of an entrepreneur and a bit of a gambler.
Indeed, he had financed a good part of his medical education
by betting on the horses at New York racetracks, and now
he was betting that he could convince his professional friend
Dr. Arthur Dale Console, medical director of Squibb, to
come up with the thousand dollars for the Scholander apparatus.

Squibb, at the time, was testing compounds of the Indian
snakeroot plant as a possible treatment of high blood pressure.
There were also many apparently unfounded folktales of the
snakeroot's effectiveness in alleviating mental disease. Kline
and Console thus concluded that this Indian flora deserved
some further, formal trials in a psychiatric hospital—a state
hospital. So Squibb granted Kline one thousand dollars to
begin his studies.

For more than two thousand years there had been reports
filtering down from various civilizations that the root of *Rauwolfia serpentina* was powerful stuff. In India it had been used
for the treatment of insomnia, insanity, and insect bites; head-
aches and heartburn; dysentery, epilepsy, cholera, blindness,
and fever. The leaves, juices, stems, or roots of the Rauwolfia
plant were sold to parents who wanted to soothe the teething

pains of their babies. And, of course, since the root looked so much like a snake it was also used as a palliative for snakebite.

Rauwolfia was referred to frequently in the folk literature of various civilizations. It had names like Chandrike or Sarpangandha (in Sanskrit) and Chota-chand (in Hindi). Two Indian researchers noted in 1933 in the *Indian Journal of Medicine* that in the bazaars of their country the root was called "Pagla-Ka-Dacra," which means, literally, "insanity herb." But what did they know? They must only be repeating the superstitions and old wives' tales of their countrymen. Sophisticated physicians and psychiatric researchers in an advanced nation such as the United States knew very well that such things were for witch doctors, not *real* doctors.

They knew it, that is, until 1949, when an article was published in the *British Heart Journal* that indicated Rauwolfia might be useful in treatment of high blood pressure. The report intrigued Dr. Robert Wilkins at Boston University, and he carried out systematic studies showing that Rauwolfia's action against hypertension was no fraud. And another researcher in India, R. A. Hakim, in 1953, won a gold medal for treating schizophrenia with a concoction of five different herbal substances—one of which was Rauwolfia. Further, there were reports that some of the patients taking Rauwolfia for high blood pressure were somewhat sedated when they were using the drug.

In spite of the recurring anecdotal evidence from folklore and the few bits of optimistic "preliminary evidence" on Rauwolfia, there was a general skepticism in the psychiatric community toward the use of any drugs in treating the mentally ill. Furthermore, there was considerable opposition to the practice of subjecting large numbers of patients to experimental drugs.

But such an "establishment" mentality didn't bother Kline.

He was already determining how best to embark on his studies for Squibb when another pharmaceutical firm, Ciba, announced that its scientists had isolated and synthesized reserpine, apparently the active ingredient in Rauwolfia. Kline and some associates had previously scheduled a visit with Ciba representatives for other reasons, but used the opportunity to propose that they include the new substance in the studies being planned. It was apparently an impressive presentation, for Ciba granted the researchers three thousand dollars.

First things first, Kline reasoned, and although every bit of evidence available indicated that neither Rauwolfia nor its extract carried the risk of significant side effects in moderate dosage, something more was needed. So in the tradition of other clinical medical researchers, Kline and several colleagues each served as volunteers to take a course of the drugs for several weeks. Then there were some preliminary trials, this time on four patients—two schizophrenics and two manic depressives. There were no major untoward effects, Kline reported, and the patients "showed no marked change in behavior beyond becoming somewhat quieter."

The road seemed clear for a large-scale study of the drugs. A carefully controlled experimental design was established and initiated.

"We started with about seven hundred patients and ended up the study with data on a little more than four hundred who had completed the trial on Rauwolfia, reserpine, and on a placebo. We had a good experimental design, good statistical analysis, and so on," Kline recalled.

In the eventual tabulation of results Kline and his associates were careful to use strictly objective measurements. They didn't want anybody to argue that they were prejudiced in assessing patients. The psychiatrists counted how many windows were broken, how many wet packs were used, how many patients had to be sedated with other sedatives. (Rockland

State Hospital, at this time, had three full-time employees who did nothing but go around the grounds replacing broken windows.)

Indeed, as Kline observed later, it was a good thing that first experiment had been set up under such strict conditions, for the results of the initial study "were rather subtle ones." One reason was that the experimental doses of drugs initially used were many times smaller than the optimum therapeutic dosage later established. Although the early results were subtle, they were highly significant.

"Every ward that has used the drug," Kline reported, "has uniformly reported a marked decrease in the decibel (noise) level, an increase in the cooperativeness of the patients, and decidedly less need for restraints, isolation, and seclusion. Even if the drug were found to do nothing more, it has already firmly established itself in our hospital as the method of choice for providing sedation at the present time. . . . The reduction in restraints, isolation, and seclusion has allowed the ward personnel at the attendant and nursing levels to devote themselves more fully to other constructive activity than was formerly possible."

In addition to the statistical success of the drugs, there was also some very human anecdotal evidence. A few cases gave "indication that Rauwolfia may act to relieve abnormal inhibition and excessive preoccupation with the opinions of other people."

Among those early patients was a bright young attorney who had acquired the habit of simply "absorbing" whatever his wife, or anyone else, "handed out" to him. "On medication," a report of his case stated, "he became outgoing enough to throw a dish of tomatoes at his wife when he was sufficiently provoked, and he also put a stop to the browbeating from the waitress at the place where he usually ate lunch."

Another striking success of the Indian snakeroot's first formal American test against mental illness was in the case of a neophyte salesman who "had been going to the movies or elsewhere to avoid the embarrassment of making business calls and possibly being turned down." There was much less concern after use of the medication with how he might feel if rejected, and he no longer avoided such contacts.

That first paper on the use of Rauwolfia in mental patients was presented to the New York Academy of Sciences in February of 1954. It also told of marked changes in the mental state of patients who had previously suffered severe compulsive and obsessive behavior.

> M. H. was a compulsive housekeeper whose ritualistic neatness was greatly relieved by medication. A. G. is a successful businessman who is obsessed by a fear of homosexuality (despite both a wife and a mistress). This had previously prevented him from taking hunting trips (which he enjoys) with male friends. Under medication, although the ideas persisted, "they lost their drive" so that he was able to go anywhere with male companions.
>
> H. H. was a chronic "worrier." His job was such that it was impossible to attend to all details. On Rauwolfia, he reports, "I no longer 'bleed' if I don't get everything done. I do what I can and that's that." There is thus indication that, although obsessions and compulsions do not entirely disappear, the discomforting motivating drive is reduced to livable proportions.

Here it was. Good scientific proof that this age-old formulation based on the twisted Indian snakeroot "in most people brings about a change of psychic state."

The sedative drugs that had been used previously, such as barbiturates and opium derivatives, had very general effects on mental patients. They caused an overall decrease in motor-function ability and made the patients sleepy and generally lethargic. Here, however, for the first time was a "magic bullet" against mental distress—a formulation that actually "tranquilized" the patients' agitated mental state without greatly

affecting other functions. The new psychiatric discipline of
psychopharmacology had been born.

With tongue in cheek ever since, Kline has many times said
of his pioneering work with Rauwolfia and reserpine, "The end
result was every exciting—I discovered a drug that had been
in use for two thousand years." (Actually, however, Kline's
was the first clinical study of reserpine, the essential Rauwolfia
derivative, in the mentally ill.)

Old or new, it looked good to the Rockland researchers.
But the problem with these early studies was that significant
results were limited mainly to patients who suffered relatively
mild disturbances. Kline realized that a way had to be found
to get more concentrated doses of the drug into the patients'
bloodstream, and a short time later when an injectable form
of reserpine became available he was anxious to try it on a
severely psychotic patient.

Although there was no concrete reason for worry, reserpine
had never before been given by injection to psychiatric patients, and Kline had all the usual concerns. He invited Dr.
Henry Brill, deputy commissioner of the New York State Department of Mental Hygiene, to sit in as an observer for the
first trial.

After briefing Brill on the patient and the general situation,
he brought in the patient, whose family had already been told
what was known about the experimental procedure. The family was happy to go along with it. Frankly, they were quite
willing to grab at straws—nobody wanted a "raving maniac"
in the family, and that's how this patient was described.

"She believed that she was burning in hell and she cried out
at the torments that demons inflicted on her body and soul,"
Kline wrote later.

He injected the patient and waited for the drug to make a
difference. Within an hour it did. Dramatically. "Visibly and
measurably, the mania began to ebb away. She was not suddenly cured of her delusion, but the terror had gone out of it.

One had to question her closely now to draw out of her the fact that she still thought she was in Hades. And over the days that followed, the delusion itself began to fade as we continued the drug treatments," Kline recalled.

In his earlier controlled studies of Rauwolfia and reserpine compared with a placebo, the results were clearly measurable —fewer restraints, fewer assaults, and the patients seemed less disturbed. But with the injectable form of the drug, results occurred right before the doctor's eyes.

Dapper, outspoken Nathan Kline was more than willing to help spread the word about Rauwolfia, reserpine, and another psychoactive drug, chlorpromazine, which was developed in France and had been introduced in Canada by Dr. Heinz Edgar Lehmann at almost exactly the same time as Rauwolfia and its derivatives were being introduced in the United States.

With Mike Gorman, a former newspaper reporter who was head of the National Committee for Mental Health, Kline made many appearances on Capitol Hill. Once, in 1956, Gorman introduced the psychiatrist to senators as "a rather young-looking boy, but his looks deceive you. He is a bright one." On another occasion Gorman presented the forty-year-old and added, "he has only just begun to shave. . . ."

Kline relished these appearances before the nation's elected representatives. And, according to Dr. Louis Lasagna, among Kline's "greatest contributions" are "his willingness and ability to interact with influential laymen, including members of Congress. . . . Kline has been responsible for the allocation of huge sums of money for psychopharmacologic research."

On May 17, 1955, his first congressional appearance, Kline told the Senate Appropriations Subcommittee part of the reserpine story:

> DR. KLINE: Mr. Chairman, this is an extremely exciting time to be in psychiatric research. There are some of us who have been working in the field for a number of years, but relatively

few. I have been doing psychiatric research for some ten years, and until very recently it was extremely difficult to find support or help to work in the field. There are some of us consumed by curiosity to know why the mind works and how it works, along with attempting to alleviate the tremendous illness.

We gave this drug (the injectable form of reserpine) to two hundred acutely disturbed psychotic females, and when females are acutely psychotically disturbed, they really are. Of this group we found that 22 percent of these patients whose prognosis was otherwise practically nil were discharged from the hospital within a period of five to six months. This was very dramatic, because normally this type of patient would not have been discharged.

I mentioned over here that from this same building, the prior year, only 4.7 percent of the patients were discharged, and here within a six months' period 22 percent of the group who were given the drug were discharged.

There are side effects, but none of them are serious. With reserpine, and the risk that is involved, it is relatively small considering the benefits to be derived.

We then carried our researches further, proceeding a step at a time, and we used it on the admission service to take care of patients who were awaiting electric-shock therapy, since it takes five or six weeks to work them up and get permission. Of ninety patients whom we placed on reserpine simply to keep them calm until ready for electric shock, we found that two-thirds of them no longer needed electric shock when the permission had been obtained.

As a result of that, we tried to see if we could replace electric shock entirely and get even better results. Since December of last year on no patient on the female admission service have we found it necessary to employ electric shock. We are just beginning to summarize our results. Although it is too early to know definitely, the results look better than we have gotten with electric shock.

Another group of patients whom we tested are the disturbed adolescents, which constitutes a real problem. Here again we found that even with the schizophrenic children, they improved while on medication and that nonschizophrenics out of the group of fourteen, eight of them were well enough to leave the hospital after three or four months of treatment.

SENATOR LISTER HILL (D-Alabama, and Subcommittee Chairman): Doctor, of the 22 percent who were discharged within five months, I do not suppose enough time has elapsed to give any final answer, but do you think they are pretty well on the road to what we might call a normal condition?

DR. KLINE: Our estimate to date is that about two-thirds of these patients have been able to maintain their improvement without any further medication. About a third of them have slipped, but if they did slip, in every case when they were re-treated, they were brought back to their normal level. And we now keep them on maintenance doses of the drug, and they have been able to hold their improvement.

You were right, sir, that it is too short to know what the long-term picture is. It will be another four or five years before we can write anything like a definitive story. But to see patients who were formerly untreatable within a matter of weeks or months become sane, rational human beings means that the wall has been breached. So that it is now simply a matter of improving on them.

Kline's testimony was so "revolutionary" that it received wide press coverage. Howard Rusk devoted an entire *New York Times* column to these "dramatic results obtained in the treatment of certain mental illness with two new drugs— chlorpromazine and reserpine." *U.S. News and World Report* found the material so fascinating that the magazine devoted three full pages to extracts from the Senate testimony of Kline and company.

But outside of a relatively small group of physicians and psychiatrists who had closely observed and participated in the Rauwolfia-reserpine work, the "breakthrough" received little support. The mainstream of psychiatry of the day still wasn't interested, and most psychiatrists honestly believed that even the suggestion of possible drugs to ease mental illness was "quackery" of the worst sort. Orthodoxy dies hard among practitioners of the healing arts. We have seen it in the stories of the other Life Givers, and this is no exception. In a few years Kline himself would coin a word, "factifuging," to describe the phenomenon. It defines how some scientists avoid coming to grips with new facts—especially if they appear to be uncomfortably correct—while pretending to do the opposite.

Most American psychiatrists were simply stuck on the conventional electric or insulin shock treatments, or the Freudian "couch and conversation" approach to serious mental disorders. Kline's statements were nothing less than blasphemy to most psychiatrists of these schools, even though he clearly stated many times that "The drugs open a way for better therapy. They are not going to replace it, but they are going to make possible better treatment than has ever been possible in the past."

Some of Kline's best friends in the profession, in fact, tried to talk him out of publishing the results of his work with reserpine and Rauwolfia. "You are ruining a promising career," they told him. "Sure, it's all right to get grants from the drug houses, but to get up and say that kind of stuff in public, when everybody knows there are no drugs that will affect the mind . . . it's insanity."

At this time, too, Albert Deutsch, a medical writer who was an old friend of Kline's, approached him after hearing a lecture. Deutsch expressed bewilderment at Kline's belief that drugs might be directly useful in mental illness. "As a trained psychotherapist, Nate, you certainly can't be serious that the drugs themselves improved the condition."

Members of the medical professions looked with increasing suspicion upon Kline's various congressional appearances and subsequent publicity. After his early testimony, for example, the National Institute of Mental Health issued a series of press releases cautioning the public against "wild statements" by "irresponsible investigators."

When a scientific researcher makes a controversial discovery he will often ride with it for the rest of his days, devoting his time and energy to "proving" his point in the face of critics. To be sure, Nathan Kline took to the lecture circuit of medical meetings and legislative hearings. Rarely, however, did Kline spend time locking horns in debate with his critics.

Instead he stuck to the significant aspects of his work, and back at Rockland State continued to direct additional studies, not only on Rauwolfia and its derivatives but on other psychoactive drugs which had been brought to light at the same time, such as chlorpromazine. The nation's pharmaceutical firms, in fact, had begun a systematic "spring cleaning" of their closetfuls of chemical compounds, trotting out the old and the new, hoping for Kline, or another investigator involved now in similar work, to evaluate the drug for potential psychoactivity.

Kline was freely predicting that reserpine was only the beginning. Indeed, early in 1956 in a paper delivered to the American Psychoanalytic Association with a colleague, Dr. Mortimer Ostow, Kline predicted that there ought to be an opposite number to the Rauwolfia derivatives, which had quickly been dubbed tranquilizers.

"If one compound could swing the emotional pendulum down," Kline said, "then there should be another compound that could swing it up."

In their paper Ostow and Kline asked: "What would be the clinical properties of a drug which facilitated the generation of psychic energy, if such a drug could be found?"

They answered their own question: "Our hypothesis would lead us to the following predictions. It would relieve simple depression and at least the sadness and inertia of melancholia

when aggression is present. It would reduce the sleep require-
ment and delay the onset of fatigue. . . . The plethora of id
energy would make large amounts of energy easily available
to the ego so that there would be more than enough energy
available for all tasks. . . ."

Kline's pioneering work with the Rauwolfia derivatives,
you will recall, began accidentally. "I had no wild expectation
or great intuition that the stuff would work," Kline said. "I
can't claim credit for that. I did it for straightforward and
practical reasons—I needed a thousand bucks for some research work and this was a legal and legitimate way of getting
it."

But now that this experience with the newfound "tranquilizers" had developed, Kline and a few colleagues "went out
looking for the antidepressants."

If the mental ailments known as psychoses could be treated
with drugs such as reserpine, thought Kline, why not drugs to
treat the depressive illnesses as well?

In the spring of 1956 Kline delivered a guest lecture at the
Warner-Chilcott Laboratories in New Jersey. Afterward he
was invited to the laboratory of Dr. Charles Scott, a researcher
with the pharmaceutical firm. Scott had been doing experiments on mice with a relatively new antituberculosis drug
called iproniazid (trade name Marsilid). He found that doses
of Marsilid made the mice strikingly alert. They were then
given doses of reserpine to tranquilize them, but instead of
becoming calm and sedated they became even more alert and
active.

Scott "was interested in tracing the mode of action of reserpine, but I was fascinated by the experimental animal. It
looked like a sort of Supermouse, and I was glad it was in a
cage," Kline recalled.

Could this antituberculosis drug be the psychic energizer
that Kline and Ostow had postulated just months earlier?

After watching Scott's supermice, Kline decided to undertake a review of the scientific papers that had been published concerning tuberculosis patients who had been treated with iproniazid which, by the way, had already been replaced by another antituberculosis drug called isoniazid, which had far fewer side effects.

By reading the published papers on Marsilid, Kline learned that one of its least desirable side effects was a "mild euphoria." At Staten Island's Sea View Hospital, where much of the early Marsilid testing was done, doctors reported that "Patients most commonly complain of excessive dreaming, excitation, restlessness, and headache. They are often noticeably irritable."

Marsilid made the chronic tuberculosis patients feel so good that they often overexerted themselves too soon. Newspaper accounts of those early studies often carried pictures of tuberculosis patients dancing in the wards. And Sea View's medical staff joked that one of Marsilid's side effects was gonorrhea, because patients taking the drug improved mentally and physically so drastically that they got weekend passes to leave the hospital—and often came back with venereal disease.

"The evidence," said Kline, "had been right under our noses, but everybody had missed it because nobody was looking."

Actually a few medical research groups had already tested Marsilid's potential activity against mental illness. A group in Chicago found Marsilid "no better" than total therapy, so the drug's use was discontinued. This conclusion surprised Kline, who saw it as an extension of the medical profession's narrow-minded attitude toward drugs and mental health: "The experimenters were comparing a simple, easily administered medication with a difficult, time-consuming, and very expensive process that included psychotherapy. They found that the one result was no better than the other, so they dropped the drug!"

A physician in Texas tried to use Marsilid to calm a group of highly agitated patients, but it made most of them worse. This researcher almost made the connection when he noted that two of his depressed patients had actually improved, but he had been concentrating so hard on his attempts to calm the agitated patients that he missed making an important observation. Others may have made the same observation, but nobody had published their results.

As we have already noted, by the time Kline got involved with Marsilid it was rarely used to treat tuberculosis anymore. In fact, it had only been kept on the market because some doctors felt it was a superior drug for treating tuberculosis of the bone. But for that, Hoffmann-La Roche, the drug's manufacturer, would have already discontinued its sale and distribution altogether. Since the drug was already on the market, Kline and his associates were able to avoid the usual "rigamarole associated with new drugs" before testing it on patients. And with his colleagues at Rockland State, Drs. John Saunders and Harry Loomer, Kline began the clinical tests.

Seventeen chronically ill female mental patients at Rockland State were treated in the first trial of Marsilid. Nine other patients under treatment for depression by private psychiatrists were also included.

The treatment didn't produce immediate or dramatic effects on any of the patients, but the psychiatrists persisted in their belief, and in the absence of any serious adverse effects on the patients they continued administering the drug. Their persistence was rewarded, for within five weeks 47 percent of the patients had shown some improvement, and at the end of five months a minimum of 70 percent of the group of patients showed a measurable favorable response.

One of those first patients was a forty-nine-year-old woman who had been hospitalized for fourteen years. She was diagnosed as a catatonic, an extreme form of schizophrenic withdrawal. Previously the woman had been given reserpine as well as shock treatment, psychotherapy, and whatever else had been available. There was no improvement in her condition.

After treatment with Marsilid, however, "she is now polite and responsive to questioning. She is definitely more alert and outgoing and considerably more cheerful than heretofore. Instead of spitting on the floor and constituting a ward problem in other ways, she is much more cooperative and helps with the ward work. She attends socials and shows much more interest in herself, definitely functioning at a higher level. At the end of five weeks none of this improvement was evident, but she has become progressively better since that time and of late has started writing sensible letters to her sister."

Another patient was a forty-three-year-old catatonic woman who had been hospitalized for twenty-six years. "Formerly she spent most of her time lying prone on the floor, but now chooses to sit in a chair. She is definitely more alert and aware of her surroundings. In the past she was extremely manneristic with compulsive clapping of her hands. This is much less frequent although she still attends to manneristic posing of her arms and head. Her eating habits are much improved and she has gained weight. Even at the end of five weeks she no longer constituted a ward problem and has given evidence of coherence at the time of the present evaluation . . ."

Such results are especially impressive in light of the fact that most of the patients in the initial study had been hospitalized for many years, were withdrawn and "deteriorated."

Although this was a pilot study, the results after only six months were positive enough for Kline to go to work at convincing the drug's manufacturer, Hoffmann-La Roche, of its usefulness in treating depressives.

One would think that a pharmaceutical firm would quickly jump into action when confronted with such evidence. There were, after all, huge profits to be made. Kline said, however, that it didn't happen that way. One possible reason was that

Dr. Elmer Severinghaus, research director of Hoffmann-La Roche, was also directing a search for a specific antidepressive drug. He was particularly impressed with the antidepressive action of the opium derivatives and hoped to find one that did not cause addiction. When he was confronted with the possibility that a suitable antidepressant of another chemical family had long been on the stock shelves of his own firm, he was, according to Kline, "adamantly skeptical."

But one of Roche's scientists, Dr. S. Evert Svenson, had already become caught up in the exciting possibilities of Marsilid's potential as a psychic energizer. After several more unsuccessful approaches at Svenson's own firm, Kline and Svenson met "secretly" in a New York restaurant with L. David Barney, president of the pharmaceutical company. "In the flush of excellent food and wine, we were able at last to bring the matter to his attention," Kline said.

Within a year Marsilid had been used in the treatment of some four hundred thousand psychiatric patients. The drug, first of a group now known as MAO inhibitors, heightens the mental and emotional responses of individuals by increasing the supply of chemicals called amines that are available to the brain circuit.

Unfortunately a number of those who took Marsilid developed jaundice and, under pressure from the U.S. Food and Drug Administration, Hoffmann-La Roche "voluntarily" withdrew it from the market. The firm had been working on the development of other MAO inhibitors, and quickly replaced Marsilid with a new drug called Marplan.

Many physicians weren't pleased with this, since they weren't sure that the jaundice was caused by Marsilid, and it was superior to its replacement. Kline actually continued to use Marsilid on at least one of his patients who did so well with it, and so poorly with others, that the FDA granted an exception for the case.

Shortly, when Kline heard rumors of Marsilid being withdrawn from the market in England as well, he wrote a letter to the *British Medical Journal.* It shows some of his hostility toward the "establishment."

As the contact man for a gang of smugglers in these sometimes United States, I am highly disturbed by the recent correspondence in the BMJ concerning the possible withdrawal of Marsilid (iproniazid) from the British market. This drug was "voluntarily" withdrawn by the manufacturer on this side of the ocean after the big-bad-wolf Food and Drug Administration huffed and puffed a bit.

In a review of the subject carried out at that time, based on prescription audit from April 1957 to February 1958, inclusive, approximately 380,000 persons received iproniazid. Dr. Eugene Jolly of the Food and Drug Administration estimated an incidence of one case of jaundice in every 10,000 patients. Considering the usual incidence of infectious jaundice in such a population (approximately 1 in 5,000), it appeared that iproniazid was an excellent drug for protection against jaundice.

A number of small groups of iproniazid users have now arranged for friends to purchase supplies for them when they visit England and, by disguising the drug with such misleading notations as "for la grippe" or "use in case of diarrhea," they have been able to get it past the customs. If the source of supply in England is dried up, we may soon find ourselves in underground commerce with the Russians, since the drug is still made there as Iprozid.

Gregarious, whimsical, insatiably curious, articulate, sardonic, annoyingly energetic, totally self-assured. These are a few of the adjectives writers have used to describe Nathan Kline. Add that he is "an audacious, utterly forthright, and happily controversial individual," and "bright, voluble, and irrepressible," and one begins to get an idea of the kind of impression conveyed by this wiry, five-foot-eight-inch psychiatrist topped with a thick thatch of gray. "I was born with the gift of laughter and the sense that the world was mad," Kline says.

The birth was in Philadelphia in 1916; his father owned a department-store chain. Nathan was second youngest of ten children—eight of them half-brothers and -sisters. He was brought up in Atlantic City, and after editing his high school's yearbook and captaining the local debating team he arrived on the doorstep of higher education. At eighteen he was a sometime writer of sonnets waiting to begin studies at Swarthmore College.

Kline would probably have followed his early impulse and become a psychologist if it hadn't been for psychiatrist Dr. McFee Campbell, one of his professors at Harvard Graduate School, where he majored in psychology for a year. "For God's sake, Kline," urged Campbell in his Scottish burr, "go to medical school. I've never met a psychologist who didn't have an inferiority complex."

Kline certainly didn't have one, so the advice was taken, but study and work requirements at New York University's Medical School didn't jive exactly with Kline's expectations. "In the honors courses at Swarthmore you carry two subjects a semester and meet once a week. NYU Medical School was about the world's most vivid contrast. There were exams every week; it was the most competitive kind of environment you could imagine. At the end of about three or four weeks I decided I had to go through medical school in my own way or I couldn't do it."

Doing it his "own way" Kline graduated "gloriously" in the lowest 10 percent of the class. (On his state medical boards, however, he scored a 93—five points higher than anyone else in his class.)

While a medical student, Kline had already made up his mind. He was going into psychiatric research, even though his older brother, also a physician, had warned it was "like playing poker with deuces wild."

Kline proved that the field really was just about that wild —but he managed to come out one of the big winners. And it's just as well, as far as he is concerned, that he never made it as one of the establishment psychiatrists.

"It's led to a kind of independent thinking," he says. "To tell the truth it's a marvelous feeling to know that you are right and that just given enough time you're going to have the fun of showing it. I still go around, in a kind of perpetual rebellion, looking for things that if somebody says 'it's black' I'll look to make sure it isn't white."

Because of his aggressiveness and forthright sense of humor Kline is disliked by many academicians. More than one psychiatrist has been known to tell his patients, "If you go to Kline, don't bother to come back here."

Kline's philosophy straddles the two major camps of psychiatry. But he believes that his theories are well founded and reconcile both points of view: "I believe strongly that there is no conflict between psychotherapeutic and pharmacotherapeutic techniques, and that the two should be used in combination whenever useful."

It's no wonder that some of the ivory towerists sneer at Kline. Just look at how he pulls the leg of academia. In a 1959 article in the *Journal of Psychology*, "Psychochemical Symbolism," he wrote several highly technical paragraphs in impeccable medical jargon and followed them with:

> As I am sure you recall, the problem which faced Kekule was how the six carbon atoms were joined or linked to each other. The solution occurred in a dream in which he visualized these six carbon atoms and perceived the bonds between them as writhing snakes.
>
> The symbolism here is so rampant that it need bear no discussion. The resolution of this multiple phallic symbolism was achieved, as was inevitable, by a gross displacement and symbolic transvestism in the creation of a symbolic vagina— the benzine ring.

Such iconoclasm has kept Kline on the outs with most of the academic psychiatric establishment, which usually takes itself far too seriously anyway. Indeed, more proof of this is that Kline has received most of his awards, including two prestigious Lasker Awards, from the nonacademic community, one for his reserpine work and a second for the psychic energizers.

The drug revolution for the treatment of the mentally ill was not all Nathan Kline's making, but his was a crucial role. The citation for his second Lasker, in 1964, told the story: "Literally hundreds of thousands of people are leading productive, normal lives who—but for Dr. Kline's work—would be leading lives of fruitless despair and frustration."

There is firm evidence of that statement's truth. The mental hospital population in the United States was 559,000, the year before the general introduction of reserpine and chlorpromazine. By 1974 the mental hospital population in the United States had shrunk to 216,000. If the old pattern of an annual upward trend in the resident patient population had not been interrupted in 1955, there would have been well over 800,000 patients in our mental hospitals in 1975 instead of a third as many.

Thus Nathan Kline theories and discoveries have offered new lives to many thousands of people who formerly had been relegated to live much of their lives in mental institutions.

7 JOHN ROCK:
The Catholic and the pill

It started thousands of years ago when some early healer packed together a few bits of dried, chopped stems or roots from a sacred plant or flower and gave it to an ailing patient. That would have been the first pill. In the ensuing years our ingenious chemists and medical men have provided us with many thousands more.

Some of those pills, à la Nathan Kline, can tranquilize the overwrought or energize the lethargic. Others rid us of the greatest killers the world has ever known—the deadly microbes that cause wounds to fester and once killed people like DDT kills mosquitoes. Still other pills ease our ubiquitous aches and pains of every description.

Of all those pills, why did it happen that only one of them became known, as *the* pill? And that one, *the* pill, really cures . . . nothing. It simply prevents the blessed state of pregnancy in the female of our species.

Is not the notoriety of this pill, a fraction the size of an aspirin tablet, somewhat surprising? Physicians have developed operations to fix our damaged hearts, repair our broken bones, ease our tremulous limbs, and remove cancers that grow deep within our bodies. Yet none of these ever became known as *the* operation.

The microbe hunters have learned to inoculate us against the ravages of influenza, polio, rabies, cholera, diphtheria, and rubella. Yet none of those has become known as *the* vaccination.

Why, then, *the* pill? One might say that it was all of the medical and public health developments that preceded it that made *the* pill so necessary, much as the advent of sanitation turned polio into a killer disease. When the plagues and their natural thinning of our numbers were slowed by our increasingly "civilized" condition, man himself had to take a greater part of the responsibility for keeping his numbers contained. With fewer worries about keeping healthy, earning a living, and fighting wars, people perhaps found more time for loving each other—and when they did more children came. More mouths to feed. In the early 1950s the world's population was 2.7 billion, a century before it was half that—and the poorer, less developed areas were growing far faster than the others. Demographers were arguing whether mankind stood on the threshold of its own annihilation by overpopulation.

The development of the idea for an oral contraceptive can be traced back to ancient times when the Chinese recommended frying in oil a piece of mercury for an entire day and then swallowing it on an empty stomach. Other civilizations recommended methods of oral contraception ranging from eating the flesh of the mule (a sterile animal) to chewing betel nuts. It is not believed that any of them worked, but for thousands of years man has had other, more complicated but slightly surer methods of contraception. They ranged from African tribes using crushed roots as cervical plugs, to douches of every imaginable sort, to the ancient Egyptians, who used pulverized crocodile dung as a pessary.

Eventually even more sophisticated methods of contraception evolved. But all were fallible, all needed careful attention, few were suited to use by the uneducated. For decades contraception was not generally thought of as an acceptable subject for conversation—or scientific research—in most circles in the United States.

Nevertheless, ever since population-control crusader Margaret Sanger opened the first free birth control clinic in America in the tenements of Brownsville, New York, on October 16, 1916, she had been looking for more effective methods of contraception.

That first birth control clinic did not want for customers. Several hundred of them stood in line from early morning till late at night. Margaret Sanger knew the problems these women faced. Innumerable times in her early career as a public health nurse in New York she had climbed the stairs of filthy tenements and witnessed the agonies of desperate women who had attempted to inflict abortions on themselves because they couldn't stand the thought of adding still another child to their already large, tattered, hungry broods. Many of these women died of hemorrhage or infections from their self-mutilation. Those who lived were destined to become pregnant again . . . and again. It was the plight of people like this that led Sanger to open her clinics and brave arrests, ridicule, and jail sentences. And the problems in New York were only a tiny portion of those around the world, particularly those of the poorer, less developed areas in eastern Asia and Central America.

Right into the 1930s and 1940s Margaret Sanger continued to search, in Asia, in Europe, around the world, for a simple, inexpensive way to prevent pregnancy. She was convinced that an effective, worldwide birth control program could never succeed without that prerequisite.

Margaret Sanger was the flint that struck the spark that started the fires that consumed a sizeable group of scientists and medical men until they had developed just such a method and made it available to the public.

It started on a winter evening in 1950 as Mrs. Sanger sat with a physician and a biologist in a Manhattan living room, talking of current methods of birth control and the future.

"The trouble now is that [today's] methods just aren't good enough. They only reduce the risk of pregnancy, they don't eliminate it," she said.

The physician in this conversation was Dr. Abraham Stone, medical director and vice-president of the small Planned Parenthood organization. With his wife, Hannah, Stone had been among the early pioneers in the field of fertility counseling. The meeting this day was taking place in the Stones' apartment.

The biologist who was the object of the attentions of Sanger and Stone was Gregory Pincus, one of the most eminent scientists ever to study the mechanics of reproduction in animals. He was not particularly interested in birth control, but he was *the* authority on the mammalian egg. As codirector of the Worcester Foundation for Experimental Biology, where significant scientific work in several areas had been done over the years, he had many resources available to him. Pincus was the man, Margaret Sanger was convinced, who would be best suited to spearhead development of a viable new method of contraception . . . oral contraception.

As Pincus recalled the conversation, Mrs. Sanger "told me in the first place that during the travels she had made she had seen so much misery, so much suffering that she was more convinced than ever of the need for devising an efficient contraceptive which women could take easily. Contraceptives in the form of injections were known but apart from the fact that they were expensive, they were not easy to distribute since physicians had to administer them.

"I told Mrs. Sanger that according to my experience, the realization of such a contraceptive was not inconceivable but that it would require money to purchase all of the material, engage staff, and obtain thousands of mice, rats, and rabbits."

A few weeks after their evening meeting Pincus received

a note from Margaret Sanger: "I have $2,000," she wrote, "perhaps a little more. Will this do?"

The amount was ridiculously small, barely enough even to buy a short-term supply of experimental animals. Yet Pincus, who saw the potential of this work, immediately replied: "Yes." A short time later he received a check for $2,300.

Pincus was a biologist and had the staff and facilities of the Worcester Foundation at his disposal. But he was not a physician, and it was clear to him that he would need a physician collaborator to carry the project through to a successful conclusion. He chose a dignified and respected obstetrician-gynecologist, who also happened to be a long-time friend: John Rock.

The choice was filled with ironies.

John Rock was a Roman Catholic, an observer of his faith, who attended mass every morning and kept a crucifix on the wall above his desk. His religion staunchly opposed as immoral any method of birth control other than the rhythm method.

If you were to meet Rock he would impress you as a doctor from down home. Indeed, he was a man of true old-school elegance who, when even a single guest visited his Brookline home for dinner, demanded the finest silver and meticulous attention to food, drink, and service.

In addition, however, John Rock was among the most sophisticated medical scientists. He had an extraordinarily large private practice of obstetrics, and for years he had also been working with infertile men and women trying to develop methods of increasing their fertility. Now he was to become a focal point in the development of a drug to decrease fertility instead of to enhance it.

There were a large number of men and women involved in the development of the oral contraceptives, explains Dr. Celso Ramon Garcia, who has worked with both Pincus and

Rock and was himself one of the handful of key scientists involved with the development of the pill. "No one of them should be given the credit," Garcia said. "But if you're going to ask who worked with this idea and then who put it across in terms of worldwide acceptance, I think one would have to say it was John Rock. He convinced the average citizen that this was not only a good method but an acceptable method—even with all of its drawbacks. He never said it was the perfect contraceptive. One really wonders whether that will ever exist."

Along with his twin sister, John Rock was the youngest of five children. He was born on March 24, 1890.

"One reason I have always been so sensitive to the problems of women," Rock often surmised, "is that for my first five or six years my best pal was my twin sister. I didn't play ball or anything. I played with her. Played dolls. I even went to sewing class."

During high school Rock won a scholarship that sent him on a summer trip to South America with the understanding that the following year he would give his schoolmates lectures on the places he visited. It was an enjoyable summer; and when he graduated from Boston High School he wanted to get back to South America, so he took a job with the United Fruit Company. Within months young Rock was first promoted, then fired. Soon he landed an accounting job with Stone and Webster, a Rhode Island construction and engineering firm. By the end of five months and another promotion, however, Rock was sacked again, for incompetence.

"It then occurred to me that I wasn't as well trained in commerce as I thought. I promised my father I would go to college," he recalls.

Rock earned his degree from Harvard in 1915 and went on to Harvard Medical School which, he says, "was perfectly simple to get into then. I just went over there, I think there was one personal interview. And you just signed the book and you were in. It never occurred to me that there would be any difficulty getting into medical school, in spite of the fact that I had just a poor C average in college."

As a doctor-to-be, Rock decided that the two areas of medicine that were worthwhile enough to spend a lifetime working in were psychiatry and human reproduction. He had pretty much decided upon psychiatry. He realized that in order to become an effective psychiatrist he would have to learn a great deal more about people, especially women, than he already knew. His way of doing this was to begin his post-medical school training with a residency in obstetrics at Boston's Lying-In Hospital in 1919.

But, as Rock explains it, "I was three years behind my age group," and by the time he finished the residency he believed himself to be too old to continue with his schooling. It was, thought this son of a Massachusetts businessman, about time he began to support himself, get married, and raise a family. Since he had already learned obstetrics, and since there were plenty of patients for him in the Boston area, he formally began the private practice of obstetrics and gynecology in 1921. The next year he received a faculty appointment in obstetrics at Harvard's Medical School.

In 1924 young Rock started the Fertility and Endocrine Clinic at the Free Hospital for Women in Brookline, a Boston suburb. It was one of the first such centers to be established in the United States. From the beginning of his career Dr. Rock was professionally concerned with the needs of couples who involuntarily remained childless. At the same time he was also interested in the opposite problem. In 1931 he was the first Catholic among fifteen Massachusetts medical men who signed a petition endorsing birth control.

"I was flying right in the face of my beloved Church," he later said. "For it had become apparent to me that contraception is a necessary instrument for family welfare, is often essential to health and, when otherwise justifiable, does not contravene Roman Catholicism."

When he made the decision to sign that petition John Rock was taking advice that he had received as a fourteen-year-old one Sunday morning back in 1904 from Father Finnick, his parish priest. "John, always stick to your conscience. Never let anyone else keep it for you."

After a moment's pause Father Finnick added, "And I mean *anyone* else."

Later in his medical career Rock once prescribed a hysterectomy for a Catholic patient "whose life may well have depended on the operation." However, the woman's priest told her not to have the operation for she would be breaking the law of her Church. "I tried to talk to him on the phone, but he was adamant," Rock recalls. "So I sent a detailed letter to the chancellery, and they told me to proceed with the operation. I can't understand stuffed shirts like that priest who think they know everything."

Like his friend Gregory Pincus, Rock was also fascinated by the mammalian egg and its development. In the mid-1930s, just after reading Aldous Huxley's *Brave New World,* he decided to try to fertilize the human egg in the laboratory, in wombs of glass instead of flesh and blood. With his associate at Harvard, Miriam F. Menkin, Rock worked for years toward this goal.

Each Wednesday Mrs. Menkin would wait outside the operating room in which Rock was performing surgery. She would receive the ovaries from patients who needed to have them removed for medical reasons. Rock had scheduled the operations to coincide with each patient's normal time of ovulation, and Mrs. Menkin took the ovaries back to the laboratory. Using special instruments, she spent hours patiently hunting for mature human eggs. Once harvested in this way, the eggs were mixed with human sperm cells and incubated in the laboratory.

One day after nearly six years of this tedious routine Mrs. Menkin came upon what she later called "the most beautiful sight ever." It was an egg that had divided into two, thus beginning the postfertilization process of growth and development. Unfortunately in the process of preserving it, the tiny two-celled embryo was lost. Just a few days later she found another fertilized egg. This time she successfully preserved and kept it.

With Dr. Arthur Hertig, Rock also recovered and preserved a series of thirty human embryos from two to seventeen days after fertilization—a group of embryos that became classic, whose pictures were studied by scientists and students throughout the world. Rock explained how he obtained them:

"Mrs. Menkin used to go over the list of women at the Free Hospital's out-patient department who had been put on the list for hysterectomy for other pathological indications. Mrs. Menkin and I would then follow these women for several months—they kept temperature graphs for us—until we got their menstrual cycle right. Then I would tell them the month they were going to be operated on. I told them that they didn't have to practice birth control or omit coitus during that month since the uterus was coming out anyway, so they couldn't get pregnant. Then I would schedule their operations in accordance with their ovulation. And so we collected the fertilized eggs. Out of those women we operated on we got the famous series of thirty eggs in various early stages of fertilization."

This work gave Rock international recognition in the field of reproductive physiology. It also put him in the hotseat as far as the Roman Catholic Church was concerned:

"The Church had great fun with that work. They called it planning an abortion. But the more superior theologians said it wasn't an abortion because the uterus was scheduled to come out anyway."

By this time, "with increasing frequency," Rock had become "disturbed by the realization that the voice of my conscience was not always telling me what the priests of my church kept saying were its dictates regarding human reproductive functioning—what was right and what was wrong in how a person willed, or permitted, or prevented expression of his God-given sexuality."

Rock was never particularly close-mouthed regarding sex and reproduction. His discussions, though completely within the bounds of good taste, were frank, and he frequently discussed his work with his wife, Anna Jane, and his four daughters and son. One of his daughters recalled that when she and the other children were growing up they often discussed Dad's work at the dinner table.

"I don't know how old I was at first, maybe five or six. Just as soon as we were old enough to eat with the grownups. Some of our dinner-time discussion was known to curl the hair of certain guests."

The conventional contraceptives being used in the late 1940s all depended on physical barriers that, under ideal circumstances, would prevent the union of sperm and egg. Too often these contraceptives failed because the barriers simply weren't efficient enough. Also, they had to be used regularly, with meticulous care by the people involved. Their effectiveness wasn't helped by the fact that at the very time the people using them needed to be thinking about contraception most, they were otherwise preoccupied.

Margaret Sanger and her Planned Parenthood supporters, therefore, were interested in the development of a contraceptive that did not depend on a physical barrier to fertilization and all of the related negative aspects of such methods. They were most interested in a physiological approach to contraception. They talked of a drug that would temporarily make either the male or the female infertile. It would have to be safe, inexpensive, effective, and relatively simple to use. This was the problem that Abe Stone and Margaret Sanger had originally presented to Gregory Pincus that night in 1950.

Once he returned to his laboratories at the Worcester Institute in Shrewsbury, Pincus enlisted the aid of a laboratory associate, Dr. Min-Chueh Chang. They critically discussed the idea of a physiological contraceptive, noting that in every normal pregnancy a woman's body temporarily becomes immune to further impregnation. This takes place because as soon as a fertilized egg implants itself into the wall of the womb, the female body steps up its production of progesterone, one of the major female sex hormones. This progesterone causes the woman's ovaries temporarily to stop development, and no new eggs are released throughout the remainder of the pregnancy. Perhaps, Pincus and Chang thought, they could also use nature's method to suppress ovulation in women who *weren't* pregnant. Actually this wasn't a completely new idea. Back in the 1930s Dr. A. W. Makepeace and other scientists had noted that when progesterone was injected into rabbits ovulation was inhibited. At the time, however, progesterone cost something like five thousand dollars an ounce. So the financial aspect of the idea didn't work, and furthermore, a contraceptive that had to be injected by a physician didn't seem to be that much of an improvement over what was available. Perhaps, Pincus and Chang thought, they could administer the drug by mouth.

To test the feasibility of this hypothesis, Chang, who relished handling the laboratory animals, began to feed progesterone tablets to a group of female rabbits. Those rabbits had other ideas, though, for they spat out the tablets. Their lack of cooperation forced Chang to revise his procedures slightly, and he soon began to administer the hormone in a liquid solution. The day after the rabbits swallowed the progesterone-containing fluid Chang moved them into mating cages where male rabbits waited. After the rabbits did what rabbits are supposed to do under such circumstances, Chang analyzed the results. The animals that had been given the smallest amounts of progesterone, less than two milligrams, continued to multiply, producing large litters. The animals that received slightly larger doses weren't quite as fertile, and only a few of them became pregnant. But the really significant news was that among the rabbits that received the largest dose of progesterone there wasn't a single pregnancy. Thus Chang and Pincus ably duplicated the earlier work, confirming that ovulation was completely halted in female rabbits when they were given sufficiently large doses of progesterone.

The Worcester Institute scientists next tried a similar experiment with laboratory rats, whose menstrual cycles are very similar to humans' except the rats have much shorter cycles. First the scientists studied a group of rats breeding under normal circumstances—the females became pregnant in about five days. A second, similar group was set up in the same breeding circumstances, but this time each of the white rats received an oral dose of between 5 and 50 milligrams of progesterone. After being given the hormone it took more than ten days for these rats to become pregnant. In other words, the single dose of progesterone had been powerful enough to suppress ovulation for at least one cycle.

Through this series of experiments Pincus and Chang proved the feasibility of using progesterone to inhibit ovulation in female laboratory animals—indeed, they had developed a very crude oral contraceptive. But at this stage in its development there was little doubt at all that this was a contraceptive for rats and rabbits, not people.

Pincus and Chang didn't know it, but less then forty miles away from their Shrewsbury laboratories, in the Boston suburb of Brookline, John Rock was using doses of female hormones to tackle a completely different problem.

At his clinic in the Free Hospital for Women the tall, pipe-smoking pioneer specialist in human fertility problems was helping an increasing number of supposedly barren couples conceive. Stories of Rock's successes in treating the infertile became almost legendary. He was virtually worshiped by many of his previous patients—and his patients-to-be as well.

Once a childless but hopeful couple from Rhode Island had a very difficult time making an appointment with Rock at his clinic. When the doctor was available the couple could never make it to the office, and when the couple had made an appointment the doctor seemed always to be unavoidably called away. This tragicomedy of unfortunate scheduling went on for months.

"I had a long letter from the fellow a few months later," Rock recalled. "He was writing to tell me—quite seriously— that my 'absent' treatment had worked. He didn't know how *I did it,* but my treatment certainly was effective and his wife had become pregnant."

Rock was the kind of physician, a colleague recalled, who really kept track of his patients. "If a patient didn't keep an appointment it wasn't just, 'Well, she didn't keep it.' He had his secretaries call that individual, track her down, and find out why she didn't keep the appointment. If a patient had been seen by a physician elsewhere, Rock wasn't satisfied with asking her to get the medical information. He would get his staff to locate the other doctor and find out what had been done and why, and all the rest."

In his work with infertile couples Rock took nothing for granted. He found, for example, that "a good percentage of the supposedly infertile women were really married to infertile men." Thus Rock emphasized the "bipartisanship involved in conception," something no other clinic had done to that time. And whether the infertile party was the male or the female of the family, Rock was able medically to alleviate the barrenness in an increasing number of couples in whom the infertility could be linked to a specific cause.

However, Rock and others working in the field were

stumped by a relatively large number of couples in which there seemed to be no specific cause for the infertility. Encouragement to try and try again was all the soft-spoken physician could give to these anxious couples.

But John Rock was not the kind of physician who was put off by such problems. He had a firm persistence and inquisitiveness about him. He paid special attention to tiny details. He instilled in his students the idea that if you didn't get an answer to a problem you persisted; you tried to solve it using whatever resources were available.

Consistent with these traits, Rock constantly kept stubborn problems under review. He looked them over time and again, especially those that had fallen by the wayside upon earlier examination.

And these couples, barren with no apparent cause, were among the most stubborn medical problems Rock had encountered in his practice to date. So he reviewed. He kept looking over the records of those hundreds of patients and he eventually noticed that the women in many of these couples suffered from hypoplasia, a condition in which the uterus and the fallopian tubes (which bring eggs from the ovaries to the womb) were underdeveloped.

As a well-trained obstetrician and gynecologist, Rock was aware that when a normal woman becomes pregnant, the rise in her body's output of the female hormones estrogen and progesterone causes a significant increase in the size of both the uterus and the tubes. Perhaps, he thus reasoned, a "false pregnancy" stimulated by supplemental doses of those two hormones would stimulate the growth of the womb and its tubes and correct the problems, making pregnancy easier to achieve.

As Rock recounted the first experiment in which he tested this theory: "Eighty childless patients agreed to try treatment with added natural hormones, known to be harmless. Daily, for three months, they took massive doses of them. The women had some of the signs and symptoms of a genuine pregnancy. For instance, they did not menstruate during the months of treatment, the breasts and, in some cases, the uterus seemed to become larger. After treatment was discontinued, menstruation recurred, and within four months, thirteen of the women became pregnant."

This phenomenon soon became generally known as the "Rock rebound." It was, however, a description of which Rock wasn't overly fond. He simply couldn't be sure that it really was a "rebound" reaction. Perhaps, he thought, the benefit simply came from the resting of the female organs— much as a tuberculosis patient benefits from a temporary collapse of an affected lung. Too, perhaps the results were misleading, since his sample of women was quite small and some of the pregnancies may not have really been related to the medication.

Nevertheless, this general mode of therapy for women with the specific problem seemed promising, although it caused some real emotional problems for the patients. First of all the pseudopregnancies caused by the hormones were so real— replete with early-morning nausea, enlarged, tender breasts, and missed menstrual periods—that the women and their husbands underwent palpable emotional shocks and had to be continually reminded that they were not actually becoming parents and that there was little chance that the hormones were harming them. Secondly the doses of the natural hormones required were so large, and thus so expensive, as to be impractical for widespread use.

Fortunately, at about this time, Pincus and Rock, old friends who hadn't been keeping right up to date with each other's activities, met at a scientific conference. With some excitement they learned of each other's recent work and compared notes and exchanged ideas.

It can be said with some certainty that in his work Pincus had not considered the possibility of hormone treatments valuable to the infertile.

It is a somewhat more controversial question, however, whether Rock had actually contemplated the possible contraceptive actions of the hormones until he met with Pincus and discussed the matter.

As practical and as thorough a physician and humanist as John Rock is, however, it is a good bet that he was well aware of the contraceptive potential of the chemicals with which he was working. "When the process of reproduction fails," he once noted, "we try to discover where there is a fault. What started it? When the fault in the chain is found, one tries to rectify it, to weld the chain together, for women who want to conceive. Conversely one seeks harmless ways to create the fault for women who don't."

Dr. Celso Ramon Garcia, who was soon to become Rock's closest professional associate, observed that "A variety of individuals have raised the question as if Rock was completely unaware that he had achieved a contraceptive modality just because he wasn't claiming it as such. These critics have to remember that we were working in the Commonwealth of Massachusetts, where it was illegal at that time to do anything about birth control. Rock felt that it was more important to be a contributor to a scientific *arbeit* than to try to fight the political turmoil."

Garcia's view is also strongly backed by the fact that Rock, as long as twenty years before, had been on record as showing significant interest in birth control. And as an observant Catholic had for years been teaching the rhythm method of birth control to his patients.

At any rate, when he returned to Boston and another try at stimulating the rebound reaction in his infertile patients, Rock this time used progesterone alone. And at Pincus's suggestion, to avoid the unfavorable physiological reactions of his patients to the missed menstrual periods, Rock told his patients to begin taking the pills the fifth day after the start of their menstrual period, take them for twenty consecutive days, and not to resume again until the fifth day after the next period.

The resultant "periods" were really false ones, since actual ovulation had not taken place. However, they served to ease the psychological traumas associated with a total lack of menstruation.

This time Rock chose twenty-seven of his chronically infertile women patients and explained to each of them the experimental nature of the treatment. First each woman was kept under close watch for a month. During this time her temperature curves were charted, vaginal smears were taken, and other tests to prove normal ovulation were carried out. When these normal characteristics were established each patient began the twenty-day course of oral progesterone tablets, and during the month of medication each patient reported as usual for the various tests. This time the data indicated that almost all of the women had stopped ovulating, but none of them were experiencing the severe pseudopregnancy symptoms of the women in the first group who had used estrogens in addition to the progesterone. After each twenty-day cycle of medication was completed, each female in the study began menstrual bleeding.

The twenty-seven women continued this regimen for two or three months each, and within four months after the medication was stopped, four of the twenty-seven became pregnant. This experiment seemed not only to confirm the rebound effect in the infertile, but to prove what Pincus and Chang had already found to be true in their laboratory animals—that progesterone could temporarily inhibit ovulation.

This experimental treatment, however, left several things to be desired. One, which bothered Rock, was that while the women took the progesterone a fifth of them suffered "breakthrough bleeding" or small episodes of bleeding between menstrual periods. Pincus wasn't satisfied with the progesterone because it wasn't sure enough in its inhibition of ovulation—it worked only in about 85 percent of the women. And tremendous doses of the expensive progesterone were required when the hormone was administered orally. What Rock and Pincus needed was a hormone or hormonelike preparation that would be as safe as progesterone but that would efficiently stop both ovulation and breakthrough bleeding in the vast majority of cases. Furthermore, it would have to be effective in tiny—and inexpensive—doses.

Pincus, who had a large number of contacts with the pharmaceutical manufacturing firms, began to ask around for samples of everything available in the way of progestoronelike steroids. Several hundred compounds were submitted, and each of them was tested by Chang and his staff in the laboratory animals. Through the fall of 1953 testing continued, and the field of those with ovulation-inhibiting potential was soon narrowed to fifteen. More exhaustive tests brought the number of finalists in this drug pageant down to three. Each of them was a member of a chemical group called the nineteen-norsteroids, a name denoting their peculiar chemical composition. Eight years before, a University of Pennsylvania chemist, Dr. Max Ehrenstein, had synthesized the first nineteen-norsteroids while looking for a substance to stimulate the heartbeat in patients where it was failing. The steroid was useless in this regard, however, so Ehrenstein noted some of its properties and filed it away. Eventually, however, the trail opened by the Pennsylvania chemist led to the development by chemists at the Searle and Company pharmaceutical firm of two compounds numbered SC-4642 and SC-5914. These were two of the three finalists that emerged from Chang's laboratory screening. The third was norethisterone, another of the nineteen-nor group. Chang, Pincus, and their assistants eventually settled on SC-4642 as the best of the batch. It was ten times more active than natural progesterone and much cheaper.

Now Pincus forwarded a batch of SC-4642—its chemical name is norethynodrel—to Dr. Rock and his "alterego" (as Rock calls him), Dr. Celso Ramon Garcia. Garcia had been an assistant professor of obstetrics and gynecology at the University of Puerto Rico, where for several years he had been cooperating with Pincus in various hormonal studies on a group of his female medical students who were interested in carrying out studies on the reproductive system and volunteered to take progesterone and collect urine samples and do other tests to assess the hormone's effects on their menstrual cycles.

Rock and Garcia enlisted the help of another group of fifty infertile women volunteers in December, 1954, for another series of fertility tests. Again the women were monitored and measured to verify that their systems were ovulating normally. And again they were put on a twenty-day course of medication, from the fifth to the twenty-fifth day of their cycles. This time, however, instead of receiving 300 milligrams of the natural progesterone, they received 10- to 15-milligram doses of one of the nineteen-norsteroids. The relatively small dose of the synthetic steroids caused far less nausea and other side effects than the natural hormone. Furthermore, when taken on the twenty-day schedule what looked as if it were a normal menstrual period appeared regularly. Breakthrough bleeding was eliminated and *all* of the women temporarily stopped ovulating. Within a few months after discontinuing use of the medication, six of the fifty highly infertile women became pregnant.

Reporting on this work in the medical journals, Rock noted with typical restraint that the results "seem to be of at least passing interest."

Now many more questions arose and were discussed among the researchers. The volunteer patients from Rock's practice had taken the synthetic progesterone medication to enhance their fertility without even the thought of contraception. And these women, too, were generally sophisticated and well educated. Would the motivation be the same for women desiring to *avoid* pregnancy rather than induce it? Could uneducated, even illiterate women—such as women in the most underdeveloped and overpopulated areas of the world—learn to use this medication properly, remembering to take their pill every day and thus take advantage of the maximum potential as a contraceptive?

More tests, widespread tests, would provide the answers. The studies in Brookline, Worcester, and elsewhere had established the basic safety and potential effectiveness of the new method of contraception. And in 1956 Rock and Garcia began large-scale studies of oral contraception in Puerto Rico. Garcia, who knew the territory, language, and people well, became the on-the-spot supervisor. Puerto Rico was an excellent testing ground for the new contraceptives, since relatively stable population areas could be isolated. There was a high fertility rate among the population and there were large segments of the population that lacked formal education— just right for testing the variables about which the researchers were most curious.

Furthermore, Garcia notes, in Puerto Rico the researchers would be able to avoid "all of the influences and politics that would be incumbent if we were going to try to set this thing up in one of the areas of the United States. First of all the laws were a lot less clearly defined. There were no laws that prohibited the use of contraceptives in Puerto Rico."

When Dr. Abraham Stone and Margaret Sanger had first approached Gregory Pincus back in 1950 Stone read Pincus a description of "the perfect contraceptive," that he and his wife had written fifteen years before: "The ideal contraceptive still remains to be developed. It should be harmless . . . entirely reliable . . . simple, practical, universally applicable, and esthetically satisfactory to both husband and wife."

With well designed and executed field studies in Puerto Rico, Pincus and Rock would soon learn whether their oral contraceptive pills would fill the bill.

Since the organized sector of Puerto Rico's medical profession was initially opposed to the study, the American researchers bypassed the establishment doctors and went to Dr. Edris Rice-Wray, medical director of Puerto Rico's family planning association. Dr. Rice-Wray was also the public health officer for several of the suburban housing projects near San Juan and thus had excellent facilities for carrying out the field studies that were needed. The first field trial thus began early in 1956 in a slum-clearance area of Rio Piedras.

Word spread quickly among the people of Rio Piedras that a lady doctor had a pill that, she said, would help them limit the size of their families. Each woman who volunteered received a physical examination and those in good health received a small bottle of twenty tiny Enovid pills—Enovid was the new brand name of norethynodrel, or chemical SC-4642. They were told to take the pill once a day, beginning five days after the onset of the period, until there were no more pills. When the women returned for a new supply, the field workers were able to conduct continuing interviews with regard to any problems that might have arisen. Each volunteer was warned as to the possible physical side effects—dizziness, diarrhea, or abdominal pains. And even though most of these women had rejected other types of contraceptives because they were too much trouble to use, 265 women volunteered to take a tablet a day for twenty days each month.

After a six-month trial—more than one thousand seven hundred menstrual cycles for these women—none of those who had taken the pill *as directed* became pregnant. There were a handful of pregnancies, but each was traced to one or more skipped pills or a misunderstanding of some sort. A few of the women used the pills only when their husbands were at home, and one volunteer couldn't understand why she had become pregnant even though her husband had faithfully taken one each morning.

"The drug," concluded Dr. Rice-Wray, "has given one hundred percent protection against pregnancy in ten-milligram doses taken for twenty days each month."

One footnote to the history of the pill occurred because of a slight error in the synthesis of the early batches of Enovid. Readers will recall that when Rock switched his patients from the combined estrogen-progesterone medication to pure progesterone, he noticed "breakthrough bleeding" in about 20 percent of the women. This problem had been eliminated when the early batches of Enovid were used. In the later batches, however, breakthrough bleeding again became a problem.

Researchers quickly traced this mystery to the fact that the Enovid manufactured toward the beginning of the studies had been contaminated with tiny traces of estrogen. Later improvements in the manufacturing process had eliminated the traces—the mistake that had actually brought the pill closer to perfection than had been realized by preventing the breakthrough bleeding. From then on the manufacturers replaced— deliberately this time—that trace of estrogen in the makeup of Enovid.

After the initial Rio Piedras study there were more field studies in Puerto Rico, as well as in Haiti, Los Angeles, and elsewhere. They all came up with similar conclusions. Some of them were voiced by the University of California Medical School's Dr. Edward Tyler, who had supervised a five-year trial on 562 women without a single pregnancy. At a 1961 medical meeting he said, "I must admit very frankly that our initial attitude toward the oral progestin method of conception control was one of skepticism. . . . But I will also confess that my opinion is continually changing. The longer our studies proceed, and the more we see long-term users of these progestins, the more impressed we are with their effectiveness and their usefulness as a method of contraception."

In May of 1960, the U.S. Food and Drug Administration approved Enovid as a contraceptive, for use on the prescription of a physician.

After the pill went public in 1960 John Rock eased up on his scientific and medical work and began in earnest, as Gregory Pincus has said, "his mission to convert the Catholic Church on birth control."

In his 1963 book, *The Time Has Come,* and in a schedule of speeches, lectures, and articles that would exhaust most men half his age—he was seventy-three in 1963—he continued his struggle to convince the Church that the pill is simply an "adjunct to nature" and therefore is not one of the "unnatural" methods of birth control proscribed by his Church.

His argument is based on the fact that the birth control pills he helped to develop, when taken daily for twenty days, effectively inhibit ovulation and prevent release of an egg that ordinarily would break loose from the ovary and pass into the fallopian tubes, where it might be fertilized. "If there is no free egg and no fertile period," Rock contended, "there is no contraception. The pill modifies for the egg the time sequence in the body's functions and stretches out the infertile period. It is this infertile period which is the theological basis of the rhythm method approved by the Church."

In a 1965 article in the *Journal of the American Medical Association* Rock asked: "What possible immorality can there be in artificially limiting the output of these glands when it can be of no service anyway? No one objects to the prevention of otherwise more useful but sometimes unesthetic output of axillary sweat glands."

When Rock's book was published and he began the usual promotional tour of radio and TV talk shows and local appearances he had an unusually active schedule. The tweed-jacketed, ruddy-faced physician, after all, was an eminent and observant Catholic who was advocating use of the oral contraceptive as an adjunct to nature and therefore compatible with the Church's position on natural means of contraception.

The *Pilot,* Boston's Archdiocesan newspaper, warned Dr. Rock to "watch his step or else."

But Rock, following his conscience, was not intimidated. "I told them they couldn't excommunicate me. It was my Church as much as theirs," he said, adding with a grin that the editorial was published while Boston's Archbishop Richard Cardinal Cushing—who was rather sympathetic to Rock's beliefs—was out of town. Cushing later wrote in the *Pilot* of Rock's inadequacies as a theologian but stressed that "in his book there is much that is good."

The New York Times later carried a story quoting a Cushing associate who said that the Cardinal's review was "a slap on the wrist—and two pats on the back," for Rock.

Whether Rock was speaking to a group in St. Louis or Schenectady, he continued to drive home his point, particularly to the Catholic community: "This is no time to stop and fuss about the right and wrong of contraception. There is nothing but right with it."

Rock's long-time experience as an obstetrician had convinced him that "child spacing is a very serious matter. I would therefore bid irresponsible, and uninformed or poorly informed zealots, however well-intentioned, to cease their presumptuous intimidation of conscientious parents by wishful speculation," he wrote, by way of scolding critics within the Church.

By 1968 Rock had raised such a ruckus that sufficient
pressure had built in the world's Catholic community to have
forced some kind of statement by the Church. Late that summer Pope Paul VI issued an encyclical in which he renewed
the prohibition against all artificial forms of birth control—
including the pill.

This came as a surprise to many who had expected the
Church to ease its position. "I was scandalized," Rock said.
"Given the transparency of the requirements of mankind, one
hardly expected the avowed leader of Christianity to abdicate
so completely responsibility for the ultimate welfare of all,"
he added, alluding particularly to the world's continuing overpopulation crisis.

Dr. Rock, saddened as he was, remained optimistic, re-
minding observers that when Galileo declared that the earth
revolved around the sun, "the Church delayed application of
his scientific insights for human benefit. But the delay was
slight, really, and the truth eventually triumphed."

Even with the Church's antipill stance, Dr. Rock notes that
large numbers of Catholic women are using the birth control
pill anyway. "If a woman, particularly a wife, went to con-
fession and told the priest she was using the pill, I feel he
would say, 'And what else?'"

Nevertheless, there remain officials within the Church who,
as Rock describes them, "can be stupid as all get out." Once,
some time ago, two of Dr. Rock's children were hitchhiking
outside of West Roxbury, Massachusetts. A priest picked them
up and during the ride he asked their names. When he heard
their replies he pulled his car to an abrupt halt and told them
to get out.

"I cannot in good conscience give a ride to the children
of John Rock," the priest said.

That was some statement, since it was the "good conscience"
of John Rock and others like him that helped start the birth
control revolution in the first place. And because they did,

millions of women have exclaimed, "You have changed my life. You have ended the fear and uncertainty." Today the families of those women can plan and space their children according to their own desires.

8 EPILOGUE:
The Life Givers revisited

JONAS SALK

Jonas Salk's development of the first viable vaccination against polio in the early 1950s was one of the first broad-ranging medical breakthroughs reported internationally through the young medium of television. Still only in his thirties, Salk became something of a folk hero.

This had rarely happened to earlier medical researchers, and it's not surprising that all the public demands and pressures, which continue even today, would change Salk's life. In the days just after the initial excitement over the polio vaccine had calmed he spent a good deal of his time thinking about the direction his future should take. As early as 1956 he began to dream of organizing a scientific institute that would bring together professionals of various scientific and humanistic specialties to work out solutions to the problems of a world becoming increasingly complex to live in. The institute Salk had in mind would use biological research to benefit every phase of life.

Now that he knew so well the problems a research scientist often had to face, he was increasingly intent on his plan. In 1963, with a gift of land from the city of San Diego and financial help from the National Foundation, Salk realized his dream.

The poured concrete walls of the Salk Institute rise like a fortress from the oceanside cliffs of La Jolla, just outside San Diego. One senses that Salk feels protected within the walls of the concrete-gray buildings, trimmed with natural hardwood to soften their imposing nature. Salk spends much of his time here now, in a brightly lit, simple office with burnished wood floors, and walls decorated with modernistic paintings. He writes letters, prepares reports, and ponders experiments in the field of immunology and human diseases to carry out now and in the future.

Salk admits to having changed, adjusting to the new way of life that evolved for him since the days when he caused a nation to weep for joy. In the depths of his soul, however, it is possible that Jonas Salk wishes he had never been forced to leave his previous, simpler lifestyle, when he was able to spend weeks, even months at a time, in his laboratory complex, "orchestrating research," as he likes to say.

Nearby his office is a storage area. In the future, when more funds are available, it will be converted into additional laboratories for Salk Institute researchers. But now it is a storage room containing file cabinets, boxes, and old pieces of laboratory equipment. They are artifacts of the development of the vaccine against polio—immunization records of children who now have families of their own, certificates and scrolls from ladies' clubs, civic groups, and foreign governments from every corner of the globe. Such mementos may gather dust, but neither Salk nor a grateful world will ever forget them.

During five lengthy interview sessions Salk impatiently found many questions unsatisfactory because they did not cover the ground he thought should be covered. He steadfastly refuses to discuss his private life or his personal relations with family or colleagues.

After being asked one such question about his colleagues

during the polio vaccine's development, he replied: "Tell me what you'd like to write. When you ask a question like that, how would it translate itself onto a page? Suppose I would answer the question any way you like. Answer it for me yourself, hypothetically. Tell me what I would say. I'm trying to understand how your mind works. I'm trying to find out what you're trying to get out of me."

In 1967 Salk and Donna, his wife of twenty-eight years, separated. They were divorced in 1968. In 1970 Salk, then fifty-five, married forty-eight-year-old Francoise Gilot, an artist and author of the book *Life With Picasso,* in which she tells of her years living with the great artist and bearing his children.

Over the years Salk's interests have broadened, particularly to include art and philosophy. "I found out there were aspects of myself that I wasn't previously aware of, probably more philosophical and artistic aspects than I ever realized," he says.

Now he divides his time between his scientific research and other endeavors. He spends a few months each year in Paris, where his wife maintains a studio. While living there, Salk devotes most of his time to writing. His first two books, *Man Unfolding* and *Survival of the Wisest,* are distinctly philosophical, appealing to intellectuals. Currently Salk is at work on books with more of an autobiographical flavor.

Salk still spends a surprising amount of time writing and corresponding on matters directly related to the polio vaccine he developed more than twenty years ago. In fact the morning of our first interview Salk received a call from a physician in Los Angeles who had given the Sabin oral polio vaccine to a thirty-seven-year-old man.

"The next day," Salk explains, "this man had a tetanus toxoid injection. He was probably going on a trip, so he was having inoculations. He had a terrible reaction to the toxoid and he was given some prednisone, a cortisone compound that suppresses immune response. So this physician called me in a panic because cortisone is contraindicated in the presence of the oral polio vaccine."

(Since cortisone compounds suppress the body's natural immune response—the very response that is supposed to keep the weakened, but still-live polio viruses of the Sabin vaccine under control—it was feared that a full-blown case of paralytic polio might occur.)

"When the doctor mentioned that the prednisone was contraindicated I said I still thought that the live virus vaccine was contraindicated, and we talked about this a bit. The doctor was quite worried and said, 'Well, look. I've never seen a case of polio. I'm thirty-four years old, and I'm concerned about this.' He wanted to know what could be done and whether he had a reason to be concerned. I told him I would give the patient some gamma globulin to give him some immediate antibody until the cortisone effect was over with."

As one might guess from such a conversation, Salk is still somewhat preoccupied with worry over the fact that the Sabin oral polio vaccine is used exclusively in the United States and the killed virus vaccine is not generally available here. He has been carrying on a low-key campaign, but according to public health experts and pharmaceutical-firm spokesmen he is not meeting with notable success.

"Metaphorically, we can say that the live virus vaccine approach is based, in part, on fighting fire with fire," Jonas Salk explains, "whereas the killed virus vaccine is based upon insulation against fire. The use of fire to fight fire occasionally backfires. . . ."

In the past several years there have been a number of lawsuits and court judgments against pharmaceutical firms because of polio cases apparently due to live virus vaccine they had manufactured. A Texas court decided one pharmaceutical firm should pay $200,000 damages because of one child's paralysis.

The chances of such a mishap occurring are roughly one in three million. Salk believes, however, that in the not too distant future pharmaceutical firms will have to stop making the oral vaccine because of the risk of losing lawsuits. Then, the scenario goes, they will revert to the safer killed virus vaccine.

"In the absence of other voices," Salk says, "I feel a responsibility to inform the public that they can justifiably demand that the killed virus vaccine be made available—even if not manufactured in the USA, it could at least be obtained elsewhere—so as to allow them the alternative of a vaccine which is not only effective but completely safe."

HOWARD RUSK

Tall, big-boned, and heavyset, he sits behind his large, orderly desk overlooking New York City's East River. In a ritual perfected many smokes ago he carefully removes the cellophane band from a long, brown cigar and lights it.

An aura of success surrounds this man, with his thin, graying hair and sparkling hazel eyes. His personal magnetism and powers of gentle persuasion could easily have helped him become evangelist or educator, corporation president or public relations executive, faith healer or medicine pitchman —in fact Howard Rusk was all of them.

"I've never really regretted getting into the rehabilitation field," he says. "This thing has taken off now. The program would have died in the early days if a few people hadn't believed and worked their hearts out . . . but it can't die now. I mean there are too many people that believe, and there are even a reasonable number of doctors that believe in rehabilitation now.

"Still, there are doctors who are resisting; not many. But some orthopedists, for example, say, what the hell's new about this? We've always done rehabilitation. What they've always done is use physiotherapists, but they've done nothing for the emotional, social, and so forth. They haven't had the time or the concept.

"The tragedy in our field is that while more and more people are becoming interested, there are only seventeen hundred specialists in our field; there are estimated to be a minimum of seven thousand hospitals and communities and medical schools that are looking for rehabilitation people. That's why I and the people here work so hard.

"People ask me all the time, 'How do you motivate people to work so hard?' That isn't our problem at all. Once people get interested and see results in other patients who've had the same thing, they are immediately convinced. That's why the patients are such good psychotherapists. The ones who are further advanced in their program are talking about going back to school or to work or going home, and some of these people have been in bed for years. Why, we've had patients who have been home-bound and in bed for twenty years. Now they're getting up and around."

The Institute for Rehabilitation Medicine, Rusk's pride and joy, is no ordinary hospital. Visitors quickly notice the large number of staff members and personnel who themselves are handicapped—secretaries, maintenance personnel, therapists, nurses, and even some doctors. As they carry out their daily work in one of the nation's best run health-care institutes, their activity is an eloquent testimonial to Rusk's theories.

The Institute has a drivers' education program, for example, with a full-time staff member who does nothing but teach handicapped people to drive—and a patient hasn't failed the first road test in ten years.

Since 1950 the Institute has had a program headed by home economists who work with a handicapped woman while she is hospitalized, giving her ideas about how to fix up her kitchen to make life easier, telling her how she can continue to run her household even though she is paralyzed on one side. "We've been doing this for twenty-five years," says long-time Rusk associate Jack Taylor. "It's routine here. Yet visitors think, gee, that's a hell of an idea."

There is little doubt that Rusk is at his best within the Institute. His eyes sparkle like a child's when he walks through the therapy rooms, corridors, recreation areas. He frequently insists on personally guiding visitors through the place.

"As I tell everybody when they first walk through the Institute," he says, "I don't care if you look at anything else but the patients' faces. There are more severely disabled people proportionately under this roof than under any other comparable roof in the world, but this is a happy place. It's not like going into a nursing home, where people just come to die and they are kept clean and comfortable. These people here, a large percentage of them, get back into some kind of reasonably good life again."

Rusk has made such statements so many times in his life that when he is interviewed today one often feels that he has turned on a hidden tape recorder to deliver yet another replay. Indeed transcripts recorded on different days, weeks apart, contain entire paragraphs that are almost verbatim from previous interviews. But Rusk does more than simply drone on about the magic of rehabilitation. One always understands, somehow, that he is totally absorbed in what he is saying.

Perhaps that's one reason why, after all these years, he's still in demand as a speaker. In a recent talk before New York's famous Dutch Treat Club he illustrated one recent innovation in rehabilitation medicine by showing off a young man whose left arm had been amputated. The arm had been replaced with a new artificial arm. It ended in a hand that looked, even felt almost like a real one. Run by a silent motor hidden where most people have biceps, the replacement hand opened and closed by electrical impulses emanating from the remaining muscles in the arm stump. The patient, then, merely has to think his hand open or closed—much as he would if he had never been in an accident. It takes practice, and it's not as good as the real thing, but it's a darn sight better than a few years ago when crude hooks, operated by pulleylike contraptions were the best to be offered.

There have been equally striking advances in other fields of rehabilitation. Quadriplegics, for example, have presented rehabilitation experts with some of their greatest problems. Their bladders and related valves are paralyzed. They have no sensation at all from the chest down. Their hands are completely or partially paralyzed.

"If you had asked me twenty years ago what we could do for this kind of patient, I would have said that if we got five percent back into some kind of life it was pretty good," Rusk reflected in 1973. "Ten years ago I'd have settled for ten percent. Four years ago we did a retrospective study of one hundred and forty-one patients who had gone through rehabilitation and were astounded to find that fifty-three percent were back in school or at some kind of work. Last year we did a similar study and found that eighty-three percent were back in school or at some kind of gainful work."

Rusk says that the greatest thing in his career has been "the acceptance of the concept of rehabilitation. The greatest thing in the next twenty years will be greater acceptance and making it available to more people. We're just scratching the surface now, when you think there are three hundred million people in the world who are in need of a simple device or an artificial limb in order to go back to work."

C. WALTON LILLEHEI

In 1967 C. Walton Lillehei left his lifelong home of Minneapolis and the medical school with which his name and his work were inextricably linked. With seventeen members of his surgical/research team Lillehei moved to New York City, where he became chief of surgery at New York Hospital, chairman of the department of surgery at Cornell University Medical College and Lewis Atterbury Stimson Professor of Surgery.

Once settled in New York, Lillehei and company made it clear that they would continue their innovative work on artificial hearts, mechanical heart valves, and new surgical techniques. In May, 1968, five months after his student Christiaan Barnard performed the world's first human-to-human heart transplant, Lillehei followed suit.

"I guess if the kids can do it, so can the old man," he joked, referring to transplants already performed by his former students Barnard and Shumway. Lillehei's first transplant patient died immediately.

In February, 1969, he headed the team of surgeons that performed the world's largest multiple-organ transplant and the first heart transplant that took place between two hospitals. The donor was an unidentified New Yorker who had died in Memorial Hospital, across the street from New York Hospital.

Heart, kidneys, and corneas from the single donor were transplanted into five separate recipients at New York Hospital under Lillehei's direction, and the liver was transplanted into a twenty-seven-year-old woman at Memorial. The heart recipient lived sixty-four days, dying of severe rejection and infection.

Lillehei continued to press surgical frontiers, and Christmas morning, 1969, he and a team of eleven doctors and nurses removed a donor's heart and lungs together in a single unit and installed them in the body of forty-three-year-old Edward Falk, a New Jersey construction worker suffering from terminal emphysema. Three hours and thirteen minutes later the new heart and lungs took over their jobs beautifully.

The operation seemed destined for great success when on the third day afterward the patient had all of the tubes removed and was able to get out of bed, walk around, and talk to visitors. But eight days after the dramatic operation severe tissue rejection claimed Falk's life.

"You just can't venture into a wilderness," remarked Lillehei, "and expect to find a paved road. All these problems are soluble—in time. I think we should continue experimental work."

All told, Lillehei performed ten heart transplants, unfortunately without notable success. The longest survivor lived 114 days. These disappointing results, however, did not belong to Lillehei alone. It was the exception, not the rule, when the early heart transplant recipients lived a year or more after their operations.

In December, 1972, I interviewed Lillehei for a series of articles on the first five years of heart transplants. By that time some hospitals, including Lillehei's own New York Hospital-Cornell Medical Center, had banned the transplant operations.

"Unfortunately there has really been an overreaction to the tremendous publicity and promise. There was too much expectation, even by some of the medical public. Perhaps we surgeons reacted that way too."

New York Hospital-Cornell Medical Center instituted its transplant ban because of the hospital directors' disenchantment with results. But Lillehei candidly told me that it was "quite likely" that he'd do another heart transplant in the future, adding that if he suffered terminal heart disease he'd ask for a transplant himself. "I'd take a shot at it. When you get to that terminal stage of heart disease, you're near the end. Of that there's no doubt."

As things developed, however, Lillehei never did transplant another heart—at least at New York Hospital—for he left there at the end of 1974 after a messy scandal centering on his conviction for income-tax evasion in February, 1973. He was accused of omitting more than $250,000 in income from his tax returns for 1964 through 1968 and owing more than $125,000 in taxes.

The government's central charge in the five-week Minneapolis trial was that Lillehei didn't report all of his income from patient fees—some $200,000 worth. He claimed, however, that much of the income had not yet been reported because under a bookkeeping system he devised he didn't report payments as income until the year in which a patient paid the bill in full.

Lillehei's lawyers produced ninety-three patient record cards in an attempt to show that eventually Lillehei planned to account for all of the income, even though his system might have been improper.

But the government used infrared light tests to show that the cards had been altered. In virtually every case the alterations showed a balance due even though some patients testified that they had paid their bills in full and had never been billed for the "balance" Lillehei's lawyers said were due.

A number of Lillehei's former patients refused to testify, however. "I just couldn't do it. If it wasn't for Dr. Lillehei I wouldn't be here today," said Mrs. Carl Schuler of Waterloo, Iowa.

United States District Judge Philip Neville put Lillehei on five years of probation, provided he agree to perform "charitable medical services, teaching, or an equivalent allied activity for six months." Lillehei agreed to the condition and served aboard the hospital ship *Hope,* which visited underdeveloped countries to provide them with medical aid. He also reportedly owed the federal government half a million dollars in back taxes, interest, and penalties.

"I stand before you labeled as a criminal," Lillehei told

the judge before sentencing. "But I must say I don't feel like one. It's hard for me to comprehend myself as a money-hungry, conniving individual."

Lillehei's lawyer added, "Society has benefited immensely from the work of this man. Perhaps this is the time for society to recognize the debt and repay him."

After serving on the *Hope*, Lillehei returned to New York Hospital. Although he had previously resigned his posts as chief of surgery and chairman of the department of surgery, he retained his chair as Lewis Atterbury Stimson Professor of Surgery.

When I returned to Lillehei's office several times late in 1974 to interview him for *The Life Givers,* he seemed to have changed considerably from our meeting two years before. As always he was soft-spoken, gentle, cooperative in every respect, but he looked a lot older now and seemed to suffer a number of minor physical ailments.

Each time we met Lillehei wore a green operating-room scrubsuit and cap, a habit common to many surgeons who are always in and out of the operating room. The difference was, however, that through 1974 Lillehei was on sabbatical leave and wasn't doing any surgery at all.

During the sabbatical Lillehei spent most of his time working on a new textbook on cardiac surgery. With clerical and secretarial help from staff and his wife, Katherine, the project moved along well.

Lillehei talked little about his medical inactivity during the sabbatical. And he never mentioned the fact that it was a "terminal sabbatical." At the end of 1974 C. Walton Lillehei left New York Hospital-Cornell Medical Center and returned to his home—which he had never sold—near Minneapolis, where he would join one of his physician-brothers in the private practice of medicine and surgery.

Personal tragedy or not, it will be a great pity if C. Walton

Lillehei doesn't soon again join forces with a medical school where he can impart his skills and his knowledge to a new generation of medical students.

IRVING COOPER

In 1973 I saw firsthand what dystonia musculorum deformans does to a human being. While I was making hospital round at St. Barnabas Hospital one weekday with Dr. Irving S. Cooper, we visited a skinny, battered girl, twisted grotesquely in her hospital bed. Flailing her arms and legs, she moved about convulsively banging her head and limbs on the metal sides of the bed.

Her tearful mother explained that the disease had begun several years earlier, with small muscular distortions of the child's foot and leg. Doctors referred both the woman and her child for psychiatric help, for they could find no physical basis for the strange disease. Psychotherapy did not help, however, and the disease continued to progress.

When it was finally diagnosed as dystonia, doctors told the woman her child's case was hopeless. Hopeless—even though since 1953 Cooper's results had been widely known and published in medical journals and in the lay press. Unfortunately, many doctors seemed to be involved in what Nathan Kline refers to as "factifuging," and they continued to ignore the promise of Cooper's work. Then the child's mother wrote a plea for help to a medical newspaper, and it was published among the letters to the editor. "Can anybody help my child? She has dystonia."

Of the many thousands of physicians who must have read the publication, none replied. But one, who had had a dystonic patient treated successfully by Cooper years before, passed the appeal along to his patient's mother. Knowing personally the horrors of the disease, she wrote the woman about Cooper and the success he had with her own child. She told her, "Don't believe those who will continue to tell you his operation doesn't work."

From her home in the mountains of Pennsylvania, the mother brought her child to New York. Somehow, though, she first went not to St. Barnabas but to one of the city's other renowned medical centers. The chief of neurology there told the woman that nothing could be done for her child.

"What about Dr. Cooper?" the woman asked.

"His operation doesn't work," said the doctor.

Recalling the experienced mother's warning, the woman carried her child out the door—for she could no longer walk unassisted—and went to St. Barnabas.

And now the mother stood, weeping at the bedside of the pitiful creature that was her daughter. The green-clad neurosurgeon could only shake his head grimly. He had lived it all, too many times before. Within days the girl was operated on. Having learned that cerebellar stimulation can also relieve dystonic deformities, Cooper implanted one of his brain pacemakers in her head.

I'm sorry to say, however, that I cannot report on the success or failure of that case. Only days after the surgery, just as the gradual, cumulative effect of the stimulation had begun, the mother came to Cooper and insisted on taking her child home: "I had a dream that the girl will die no matter what we do." Cooper spent the better part of a day pleading with the woman to leave the child at the hospital. But his efforts were to no avail. The mother rescinded her permission for medical treatment, a decision legally within her rights as a parent, and took her child home.

More than twenty years of such frustrations led Irving Cooper to consider retiring from medicine to devote his time to writing. But that was before he began working on the electronic brain pacemaker. After the first two years of work on this discovery, he found himself torn between literary and medical worlds. His first effort at writing for the general public, *The Victim Is Always the Same,* about two of his young dystonia patients, was published in 1973, received excellent reviews, and became a documentary movie for television. Cooper had already begun work on an autobiography, a novel, and a handbook for the families of chronically ill patients.

His love for writing notwithstanding, he was well aware of the importance and the impact of his latest scientific work. "We're just beginning what will be at least a five- or ten-year study," he says. "I'm sure that a number of colleagues elsewhere will try our techniques so that many aspects of this brain pacemaker will be studied. This is an early phase of the work, and it has all the unknowns of any new work."

In 1974 Cooper packed up his young second wife, Sissel, and their two-year-old son and went off to spend four months as a visiting professor at Queen's Square Hospital in London, where he gave a series of important lectures about his work to the faculty and students.

The time he spent at the historic London Hospital was very significant to Cooper, for in his lectures he laid out and discussed his lifetime of neurosurgical work; and it was warmly received. Queen's Square Hospital has been known as the mecca of modern neurosurgery since Sir Victor Horsley, pioneer in the field, got his start there.

"One of the nicest things," Cooper said of his London stay, "was that I was also a student there. I attended all of the neurosurgical teaching rounds. It was a great privilege to become a student again."

The Londoners were also more than pleased to have Cooper as a visitor. "Cooper is regarded with intense respect and something much warmer than that by his English colleagues," according to Lord C. P. Snow.

Cooper first met the British novelist and physicist in 1972

when Cooper invited Snow to speak at the dedication of a
new wing at St. Barnabas. Snow had always been one of the
surgeon's literary idols, Cooper having devoured all of Snow's
works.

Friendship blossomed between the two, especially because
of their shared interests in the interactions between new developments in science and medicine and how they affect
humanity.

"Cooper," says Snow, "has a particular passion for some
of my favorite writers, such as Dostoevski and Camus. He
writes remarkably well in English, quite outside his professional range. He is in the process of writing a novel, which I
regard as rather unfair competition. After all, most novelists
would be hard put to perform a brain operation."

Cooper appears as an important character in Snow's 1974
novel, *In Their Wisdom*. The two are currently carrying on
an extensive correspondence concerning matters of their
mutual interest.

Upon his return from London, Cooper went back to his
research and practice at St. Barnabas—although he limits
his own surgery to a couple of times a week, now—and to his
various literary projects. Cooper also assumed a new teaching
post, as research professor of neurosurgery at New York
University. This about brings Cooper's life and career back
to the beginning of a giant circle, for as the reader will
recall, it was back in 1951 that Cooper, then a young resident,
operated on Joseph Cioppa at New York University's Bellevue
Hospital. Shortly thereafter Cooper resigned his professorship
at NYU to devote more time to his work at St. Barnabas
Hospital in the Bronx.

Now Cooper will work at both institutions as well as on his
various other projects, continuing to pursue his two pressing
love affairs—with the human brain itself and with the patients
for whom he feels so deeply.

NATHAN KLINE

At a time when most people seem to be decrying our drug-oriented society and calling the United States a nation of pill poppers, Nathan Kline sees another side of the situation.

"The basic problem," he says, "is not the overmedicated patient but the undermedicated and the unmedicated patients."

He cites studies of the international use of psychotropic drugs showing that Americans are about average in this regard when compared to other Western nations.

Other studies that Kline frequently quotes show that the vast majority of patients who use psychotropic drugs have high degrees of genuine "psychic distress" when they take the medication, thus their use is justified. On the other hand, he says, "roughly half the population that needs help is going unmedicated when drugs could provide substantial general relief for psychic distress.

"Despite the existence of some twenty thousand psychiatrists in the United States we are still grossly understaffed to deal with the problem confronting us—particularly because psychiatrists congregate in the large urban centers and substantial segments of the country are as poorly supplied with psychiatric services as the so-called less developed countries.

"I have calculated that each practicing psychiatrist should be carrying a load of twenty-five hundred patients to meet the minimal needs of the country today. Pharmacotherapy is the one and only practical solution to the problem for the major part of the spectrum of mental disorders."

Even Kline's practice, huge by psychiatric standards, doesn't come anywhere near this kind of scale. With three other psychiatrists and five nurses at his East Side offices, more than five hundred patients are seen annually. His active file contains thousands of names.

These are patients, Kline says, who are "at the end of the line. They're desperate." *Desperate* is really the best word for these unfortunate people. Most of them have seen other psychiatrists to no avail and are on the brink of collapse, perhaps hospitalization.

One of Kline's former patients, a New York public relations executive, tells how he was so severely depressed that he had begun to live a hermitlike existence. His business and personal life had begun to suffer severely. Finally a physician friend suggested he see Kline.

"I knew all of the talk that Kline was some kind of a nut who thought that pills were everything. But I really needed help, so I tried him. He took a lot of tests, gave me some pills. They changed my state of mind within weeks. I was feeling normal again. I mean to say that this treatment really changed my life. I have no doubt it kept me out of really desperate straits—like hospitalization."

Dr. Kline doesn't expect that cures will ever be found for all mental illness, just as there will probably never be total cures for all physical illness. But he believes that the drugs for mental illness that he helped pioneer will go a long way toward this end.

"One myth that bothers me is the myth of total curability," says the gray-haired psychiatrist. "In eighty percent of physical medicine we won't look for total cure—only for rehabilitation. The person who has a heart attack is never quite the same again. But in psychiatry there is a tendency to believe that you ought to keep changing therapists or therapies until the patient is absolutely perfect. It results in an unrealistic expectation of what therapy can do. Many people who are able to function quite well and get a reasonable amount of enjoyment out of life are left disconsolate and apprehensive because they haven't achieved this impossible goal."

In some conditions, such as depression, Kline says, complete remission can be achieved. "But with other disorders, such as schizophrenia, we may have to face the fact that there will always be some limitation on the person's capacity. If both he and the family can accept this fact, the individual can usually lead a pretty happy, productive life."

Kline's private psychiatric patients represent only a portion of his busy professional life these days. He spends a good deal of his time at Rockland State Hospital where he continues to direct the research program. Within the past few years he has run a massive project using computers to standardize and record the case histories of psychiatric patients. He believes that this standardization, when it is sufficiently widespread, will mark another revolution in psychiatry.

Aside from his private practice and Rockland State, Kline keeps a breakneck pace of consultation, travel, and speeches. He keeps electronic dictating equipment in his office, his home, his car, and even his briefcase, so he can use every moment of time to his best advantage. One of the series of interviews for this book took place in Kline's car, while traveling through midtown Manhattan rush-hour traffic from Kline's office to a Fifth Avenue clothing store where he had to return a suit for alterations.

"Fortunately I need only about four and a half hours of sleep. That means I don't necessarily run faster than others, I just have more time in which to run. I'm also pretty good about disciplining myself to keep things pretty current."

One of Kline's special interests has been the psychiatric care in underdeveloped nations of the world. "In countries like Nepal there is one psychiatrist for eleven million people; in Indonesia, where there are less than fifty psychiatrists for one hundred and ten million people (comparable to twenty-five psychiatrists for all of Great Britain and eighty for the whole United States); and in numerous other countries where the ratio of psychiatrist to population is one to hundreds of thousands or millions of people, it is utterly ridiculous to even think about attempting to deal with the problem by way of individual psychotherapy or even family or group therapy. It is not that these other treatments do not have a place (and a valuable one when indicated), but they are utterly impractical to deal with the mass and bulk of the problem," Kline says.

His long-time interest in the spectrum of mind-body relationships has led Kline to visit many of the primitive nations of the world. Many pieces of fascinating primitive art decorate his offices. The animal and humanoid forms, perhaps grotesque to the Westerner untrained in their meanings, testify to the different modes of thinking in other cultures.

"My main interest in going off to these esoteric places such as Sarawak, Nepal, and so on—in addition to the fact that I like to travel—is that I get to see not only how the patients behave there but get some understanding about how people think in these cultures. And they do think differently. There's no way around it. There is a lot of symbolic thinking that goes on that is quite foreign to us.

"In Africa, and not only among people out in the bush, the Africans have this great habit of having a conversation and telling you all kinds of things they are going to do. They make all these commitments. These are perfectly sincere at the moment, but if you don't know that it's just for the moment, you're going to be led down the garden path. When they get back home it's a different matter. The point is they participate not by telling you what they will do but what they would like to do.

"This is a minor difference. In many of the societies there things are really quite different. In most of West Africa and Java, for example, the people believe in the existence of ancestral spirits. It's not just kidding, they really believe it."

The psychiatrist likes to tell about the occasion when he spent some time with the Dalai Lama in India. Kline told him that he was professionally interested in depression; and he was curious to know whether the Dalai Lama didn't get depressed sometimes, since he was not only the spiritual but the temporal leader of something like thirty million people.

"He said no. It didn't disturb him at all. But he acknowledged how he could understand why people in the West become depressed—because they don't believe in reincarnation. This makes sense, after all, because if you believe in reincarnation then whatever happens is really no sweat."

Before leaving the Dalai Lama, Kline said, he was given "a really nice Tanka [a Tibetan religious painting]." And then the psychiatrist paused for a moment. "Well," he admitted, "it really wasn't very nice. In fact it was kind of a crummy one, but at least I can say the Dalai Lama gave it to me."

JOHN ROCK

"All these questions you ask . . . well, this is all very interesting material," eighty-four-year-old John Rock told me the June afternoon we first met. "I wish you had called on me before I settled into my dotage. You touch on so many interesting areas that I really used to cerebrate about, and now you see I have nothing left. I can't really get disturbed about it, because there's nothing to do. It's like a worn-out iron, you just lock it up."

Rock is the only one of the Life Givers who had retired at the time this book was being written. He lives in a brown clapboard house deep in the pine and maple woods of Temple, New Hampshire. He used the house as a retreat while he was still professionally active. When his wife of thirty-six years died in 1961, he retreated to New Hampshire with increasing frequency. Ten years later he moved in altogether.

Rock frequently gets together with his daughters and their families; he has nineteen grandchildren. "I'm not unaware of the irony of a birth control proponent grandsiring a tribe such as this, but it's a wonderful family," he observes with a broad grin.

The grandchildren are frequent visitors. In the summer they fish and swim and in the winter the house becomes an overnight ski lodge for the youngsters and their friends. "It gets quite lively around here," Rock observes. To bridge the gaps when family members aren't around, a young male companion also lives on the premises to keep an eye on Rock, cook for him, get the mail (a couple-of-miles drive to the post office, general store), and do the shopping.

When weather permits the tall, slender Rock spends most of his time a few hundred feet from the house, secluded in a small clearing surrounding a clear-running mountain brook that he once dammed for swimming. In this idyllic setting he skinny-dips amidst the trout, takes a snooze, drinks a can of beer.

When a visitor begins to discuss his work on the birth control pill Rock, his sparkling blue eyes still a match for the brook, is quick to minimize the role he played: "My name is John Rock, not Celso Ramon Garcia. If my name had been Elgin R. Magilicuddy nobody would have ever paid any attention to me. It's just these two four-letter, one-syllable words —John Rock. Nobody would even remember Elgin R. Magilicuddy," he says with a chuckle.

Gentle, modest John Rock putters around his garden and swimming hole wearing green jumpsuits, a kind of dressy overalls. Thin white hair always in place, frequently puffing his pipe, Rock hasn't given up his gracious style of living. Every evening before dinner he is presented with a cocktail shaker full of martinis—"Although I daresay they've been altered to where they're just about vermouth and ice now," he confides.

"Don't talk business, it's dinner-time," he adds, sipping his drink. He rocks for a while, then looks at his guest, again going into a short discussion centering on what seems to be his favorite word these days—*cerebrate.*

"I just don't do it anymore," he repeats. But the octogenarian always seems to come up with a particularly salient point just after making the statement.

Does he think the birth control pill has contributed to promiscuity?

"Oh, yes. It surely has. It came on along with the sex revolution, the freedom of the sexes. The premature maturation of youth . . . yes, the boys have stopped carrying condoms in their wallets as they did in my days."

He feels we will never return to Puritanism, but Rock believes that the young have reached a greater understanding of sex.

"The peak of permissiveness is passed. The radical libertarians have lost much of their prestige. The young people are beginning to realize that you can't tamper with the sexual function, for it is much more than thrills."

Is the newfound sexual freedom, with promiscuity and living together before marriage, going to be harmful to our society in the long run?

"I have always thought that sex is great fun, but it must be indulged in with regard to our social responsibilities. I think that what you call promiscuity, or premarital living together, is not necessarily good for society, but on the other hand individuals desire and deserve outlets."

John Rock lives a quiet life, and this is the way he wants it. He complains about his deteriorating senses, but is acutely aware of what goes on around him.

A crucifix still hangs on the wall above the desk in the corner of his bedroom. He still has faith that someday— soon—the Church will give in and reverse its stand on the pill.

He hasn't practiced medicine for several years, but recent

magazines and journals are piled neatly on his desk. When he jots down a note for a visitor it is, as likely as not, written on one of his prescription pads.

Rock was professionally active right into his late seventies, hopping about the country and the world, lecturing here, consulting there, writing an article for this magazine or that, jibing his beloved Church about its stand on the pill.

It's true, now, that Rock occasionally has trouble "cerebrating"—remembering much about his own work of twenty and more years ago, when together with Gregory Pincus, M. C. Chang, and Celso Ramon Garcia he helped develop and test the first oral contraceptive pill. Some grateful coeds later canonized him as "the saint of Radcliffe."

He can't reminisce much about those days anymore, but one gets the distinct impression that he really doesn't care. "I think it's all right for an eighty-four-year-old to lose hold," John Rock says. "I earned a rest."

Acknowledgments

I acknowledge with thanks each of the Life Givers, their associates, and their families, for the time made available to me in the course of this project. I am grateful to the many others who have written about them, particularly in newspapers and magazines, as well as a few books. Many of them are referred to by name in this book.

My employers and colleagues at Newspaper Enterprise Association have, as always, been tolerant and helpful.

Howard Cady, a wise and experienced editor, gave advice and confidence when they were needed most.

The Albert and Mary Lasker Foundation, the American Medical Association, New York University, the Finkelstein Memorial Library, the Salk Institute, the Planned Parenthood Federation, the National Foundation, the U.S. Public Health Service, and St. Barnabas Hospital were among the institutions that provided valuable information.

I want to thank Mrs. Mary Lasker for suggesting the need for this book, a suggestion passed along to me by the publisher.

Aaron Hendin, M.D., and Lillian Hendin, my parents, read the manuscript and suggested a number of important changes.

The comments of all of the above, and many more, were carefully considered and often implemented. The responsibility for opinions or inaccuracies within, however, rest solely with the author.

Finally the greatest gratitude is due my wife, Sandra, who, though engaged in being another kind of Life Giver, helped with all phases of the project. My three-year-old daughter, Sarah, always tried to be very quiet while Daddy worked, but couldn't resist coming in for an occasional "I need a kiss, Dad." Those kisses kept it going through some difficult times.

Index